Patterns in Math

Donald Eperson

Basil Blackwell

© 1988 Donald Eperson
First published 1988

Published by Basil Blackwell Ltd
108 Cowley Road
Oxford OX4 1JF
England

British Library Cataloguing in Publication Data

Eperson, Donald
 Patterns in mathematics.
 1. Mathematics–Questions & answers–
 For schools
 I. Title
 510′.76

 ISBN 0–631–90137–X

Typeset in 10½ pt Times
by MULTIPLEX techniques ltd, St Mary Cray, Kent.
Printed in Hong Kong
by Wing King Tong Co. Ltd.

Contents

Preface   iv

1 Number patterns   1
    Problems   5
2 Lewis Carroll — mathematician   9
    Problems   13
3 Magic squares   19
    Problems   22
4 Pythagoras and his theorem   25
    Problems   29
5 Jigsaw puzzles   33
    Problems   36
6 Prime numbers   43
    Problems   49
7 Knight's tours   53
    Problems   56
8 What comes next?   59
    Problems   61
9 More magic square patterns   65
    Problems   72
10 Geometrical puzzles   79
    Problems   81
11 Patterns in number tables   87
    Problems   87

Solutions   93

Preface

Mathematical patterns are valuable as visual aids that enable children to understand the basic ideas and vocabulary of numbers and shapes. They can stimulate curiosity and a desire to explore further by providing aesthetic pleasure, so that arithmetic, algebra and geometry become enjoyable activities.

Some of the topics in this book have been tried out in primary schools, and some in secondary schools. Others are derived from courses for students at two colleges of education. At one of these colleges I was responsible for remedial courses for students who disliked mathematics and feared the prospect of having to teach the subject in school. A new approach to elementary concepts has often cured victims of 'mathophobia'.

The ideas and activities are similar to those in my articles in the 'Maths Extra' sections of the *Times Educational Supplement*, and my regular contributions of 'Puzzles, Pastimes and Problems' in the periodical *Mathematics in School*. These have been appreciated by teachers of elementary mathematics up to O-level, as a source of material for use in the classroom to supplement textbooks.

Many recreational pastimes that involve numbers and shapes are of educational value. For example, it is doubtful whether magic squares are useful in a practical way in this computerised technological age, but they have stimulated interest in numerical relations throughout forty centuries. More recently, fascinating geometrical patterns have been discovered in them.

The simple pastime of inventing one's own domino patterns for numbers is a creative activity for parents and children familiar with numerals. It provides insight both into numerical relationships and into the two kinds of symmetry, reflectional and rotational.

The first part of each chapter contains information and examples that can be used by teachers when presenting a topic in the classroom. This is followed by 'Problem' pages for use by individual pupils at school or at home.

Donald Eperson, 1988

⬚ *Number patterns*

Before the invention of Arabic numerals, Chinese and Greek mathematicians used symmetrical patterns, such as those used on dominoes, dice and playing cards, to represent numbers.

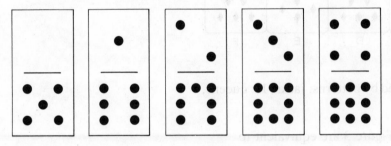

Figure 1 Domino patterns

The patterns for numbers from 0 to 9, shown in Figure 1, are used on a commercially made set of dominoes, ranging from 'double blank' to 'double nine'. Each pattern fits inside a square.

Q1 Find alternative patterns for 3, 4, 5 and 6.

Figure 2 Playing card patterns

The patterns used for the numbers 1 to 10 in a pack of playing cards are designed to fill a rectangular space. The patterns in Figure 2 show that

$$7 = 6 + 1 = 5 + 2 \qquad = 4 + 3$$
$$8 = 6 + 2 = 5 + 3$$
$$9 = 8 + 1 = 4 + 4 + 1 = 5 + 4$$
$$10 = 8 + 2 = 4 + 4 + 2 = 5 + 5$$

Q2 Find a set of playing card patterns that show that
$7 = 3 + 4$, $8 = 2 + 4 + 2$, $9 = 2 + 3 + 4$ and
$10 = 1 + 2 + 3 + 4$.

Q3 Find an alternative set of number patterns suitable for
dominoes for the numbers 7, 8 and 9 with

  a only one line of symmetry

  b two or more lines of symmetry

  c rotational symmetry only.

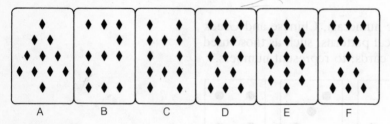

Figure 3 Playing card patterns

Court cards could be represented by patterns: jacks, 11; queens,
12; kings, 13.

Q4 Which of the patterns in Figure 3 are equivalent to

  a jacks?

  b queens?

  c kings?

Q5 Design a set of playing card patterns for the numbers 11,
12 and 13.

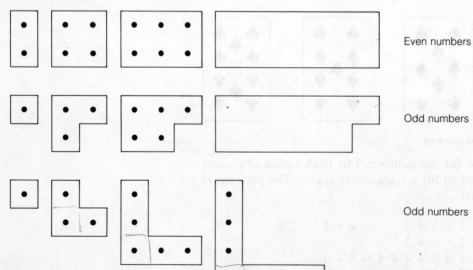

Even numbers

Odd numbers

Odd numbers

Figure 4 Greek number patterns

The Greeks classified numbers according to the shape of their patterns (Figure 4). Even numbers consisted of pairs, making a rectangular shape. Odd numbers were one more (or one less) than the adjoining even number. They could be represented either by an even-number rectangle with an extra 'unit', or by a **gnomon** (an L-shaped pattern) with the odd 1 at the corner and vertical and horizontal 'arms' of equal size.

These patterns were used to show simple number relations such as

the sum of two even numbers is an even number

and

the difference between two odd numbers is an even number

Q6   Use patterns to show that

a   the sum of two odd numbers is an even number

b   the sum of two consecutive odd numbers is always a multiple of 4.

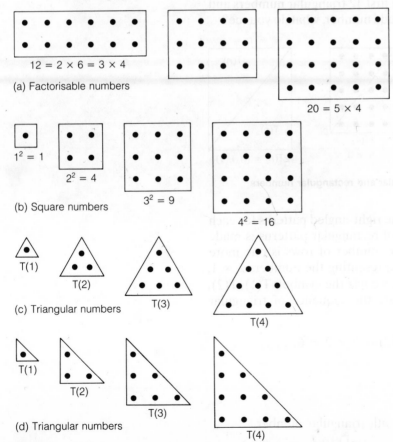

(a) Factorisable numbers

$12 = 2 \times 6 = 3 \times 4$

$20 = 5 \times 4$

(b) Square numbers

$1^2 = 1$

$2^2 = 4$

$3^2 = 9$

$4^2 = 16$

(c) Triangular numbers

T(1)   T(2)   T(3)   T(4)

(d) Triangular numbers

T(1)   T(2)   T(3)   T(4)

Figure 5 Various number patterns

Factorisable numbers (including even numbers) had a rectangular pattern (Figure 5(a)). Numbers that were the product of two equal numbers had a square pattern and were known as square numbers (Figure 5(b)). (This included 1, since $1 \times 1 = 1$.) Triangular numbers were those with a triangular pattern, either an equilateral triangle (Figure 5(c)) or a right-angled isosceles triangle (Figure 5(d)). The number of rows in the pattern was the same as the number in the longest row.

Q7 *a*   Continue this sequence of square numbers: $1^2, 2^2, 3^2,$ . . .. Find and describe the sequence formed by the difference between pairs of consecutive square numbers.

   b   Continue this sequence of triangular numbers: 1, 3, 6, 10, ... Find and describe the sequence formed by the sums of pairs of consecutive triangular numbers.

   c   Demonstrate the result in *b* by using patterns for triangular numbers.

   d   If you write down the first 12 triangular numbers and put a ring round each odd number, what do you see?

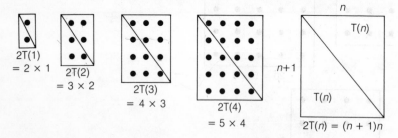

Figure 6 Relationship between triangular and rectangular numbers

By fitting together two of the right-angled patterns for each triangular number, a sequence of rectangular patterns is made (Figure 6). In each pattern, the number of rows is one more than the number of columns, representing the numbers 2×1, 3×2, 4×3, . . ., $(n + 1)n$. If we use the symbols T(1), T(2), T(3), T(4), . . ., T(n) to indicate the sequence of triangular numbers, then

$$2T(1) = 2 \times 1 = 2, \; 2T(2) = 3 \times 2 = 6, \ldots$$

and so

$$2T(n) = (n + 1)n$$

which gives the formula for the *n*th triangular number

$$T(n) = \tfrac{1}{2}n(n + 1) \qquad \frac{n(n+1)}{2} = T(n)$$

Q8 *a* How many triangular numbers are prime numbers?

b What are the prime factors of T(20) and T(100)?

c Which of these triangular numbers are also square numbers: T(8), T(9), T(16), T(49), T(99), T(144), T(288)?

Problems

1 These patterns are like the patterns used to represent numbers on dice, dominoes and playing cards.
What are the numbers shown by the patterns?
How many lines of symmetry has each pattern?
Invent your own patterns for the numbers from 5 to 9.

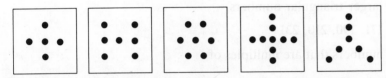

2 What sets of numbers are shown by these V-shaped and hollow-square patterns?
Invent a set of patterns which show the numbers 3, 6, 9, 12 and 15 (the multiples of 3).

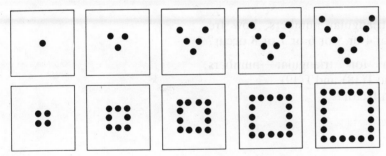

3 On playing cards, the numbers 11, 12 and 13 are represented by jacks, queens and kings. Which of the above symmetrical patterns could be used instead of

a jacks?

b queens?

c kings?

Invent patterns for the numbers 10, 11, 12 and 13.

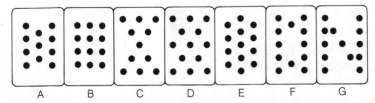

A B C D E F G

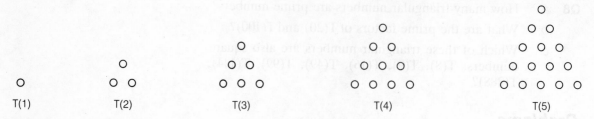

T(1)   T(2)   T(3)   T(4)   T(5)

4   These patterns show the first five **triangular numbers**.

a   Write down the first 12 triangular numbers. What do
you see when pairs of consecutive triangular numbers
are added together? $(1 + 3, 3 + 6, 6 + 10, 10 + 15,$
. . ..)

b   Copy this sequence of larger triangular numbers:

91, 105, 120, 136, 153, 171, 190, 210, 231

Draw a ring round the numbers that are multiples of
3. What do you see?

c   Is it true that in the first 12 triangular numbers there
are six odd numbers, six even numbers and eight
multiples of 3, and that the remaining numbers are
each one more than a multiple of 3? Give reasons
for your answer.

d   In the sequence of triangular numbers, how fre-
quently do multiples of 4 or 5 or 6 or 7 or 8 occur?

e   Using the formula for triangular numbers,
$T(n) = \frac{1}{2}n(n + 1)$, find T(18) and T(19).
What is their common factor?

f   Complete this table:

$T(2) - 2T(1) = 1^2$
$T(4) - 2T(2) =$
$T(6) - 2T(3) =$
$T(8) - 2T(4) =$
$T(10) - 2T(5) =$

What is the set of numbers in the end column?
Verify the result by finding $T(2n) - 2T(n)$.

g   Show that $3T(2) + T(1) = T(4)$
and that $3T(3) + T(2) = T(6)$

Simplify $3T(4) + T(3) = T(\ )$
and $3T(n) + T(n -1) = T(\ )$

h   Is it true that no triangular number has 2 or 4 or 7
or 9 as its final digit? Give reasons for your answer.

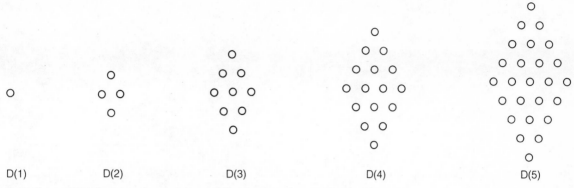

D(1) D(2) D(3) D(4) D(5)

i   Which set of numbers is shown by these diamond-shaped patterns?
Complete this table showing the final digit of each number.

D pattern number	1	2	3	4	5	6	7	8	9	10
Final digit	1								1	0

Can you see a symmetrical pattern in the second row?
Which numbers do not appear in the second row?
Is it true that every number shown by a diamond-shaped pattern is either a multiple of 4, or one more than a multiple of 4? Give reasons for your answer.

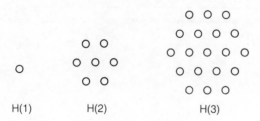

H(1) H(2) H(3)

j   What numbers are shown by these hexagonal patterns?
Find the next three numbers in this sequence. Show that they are all one more than a multiple of 6, and find a formula for H(n).
The sum of the first pair of numbers is $8 = 2^3$. What do you find by adding together the first 3, or 4, or 5 consecutive numbers in this sequence?

2 Lewis Carroll — mathematician

Humpty Dumpty was not good at arithmetic. He could not subtract 1 from 365 in order to calculate how many 'unbirthdays' there were in a year. Even the quick-witted Alice, when orally examined by the White and Red Queens in the land *Through the Looking Glass*, could not do subtraction. 'Take nine from five — I cannot'.

Arithmetical and logical allusions can be found in both of the books describing the adventures of Alice and in *The Hunting of the Snark*. Lewis Carroll was the pen-name of the Reverend Charles Lutwidge Dodgson, lecturer in mathematics at Christ Church, Oxford, who published his mathematical books and pamphlets under his real name. 'Alice' was Alice Liddell, one of the three daughters of the Dean of Christ Church.

The most widely read of Dodgson's mathematical books was *Euclid and his Modern Rivals*, in which he championed the cause of the Greek geometer and advocated the continuation of the use of Euclid's *Elements* as a school textbook. Dodgson's book dealt with a serious controversy of Victorian times, but it was written in the witty and humorous style that brought him world-wide fame with Alice.

Again under the pen-name Lewis Carroll, Charles Dodgson provided entertainment for children and adults by inventing puzzles, paradoxes, and word games, including *Pillow Problems* and *The Game of Logic*. He believed that these intellectual activities were a source of pleasure and amusement — an idea that was not generally accepted until the middle of the twentieth century.

The Game of Logic was intended for children to play with counters on a square patterned board that was the equivalent of a Venn diagram.

Years later *Symbolic Logic* was published, with more elaborate diagrams and an original algebraic notation for solving complicated problems in logic.

After 25 years as lecturer in mathematics, Dodgson continued to live in Tom Quad, planning to use his time in writing more story books for children, and a series of books under the general title *Curiosa Mathematica*.

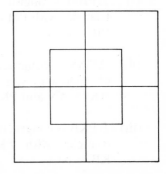

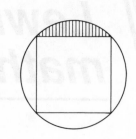

The first volume to be published was *A New Theory of Parallels* in which he enquired whether Euclid's parallel axiom were true, and based his new theory on his own axiom—the self-evident truth that the area of a square inscribed in a circle is greater than that of any one of the four segments surrounding it.

Volume 2 was the famous *Pillow Problems*, stated to have been 'thought out during sleepless nights'. These showed the author's extraordinary powers of inventing and solving mathematical problems mentally. In the preface to the second edition, the words 'sleepless nights' were changed to 'wakeful hours', so as to allay the fears of friends that he suffered from insomnia.

Would-be solvers of these samples may prefer to use pen and paper: the solutions can be found in modern reproductions of the book.

(1)   Prove that three times the sum of three squares is also the sum of four squares.

(2)   Sum the series $1 \times 5 + 2 \times 6 + 3 \times 7$ etc.

    (i)   to n terms

    (ii)   to 100 terms.

(3)   Find a point in the base of a given triangle, such that, if perpendiculars be dropped from it upon the sides, the line joining their feet shall be parallel to the base.

(4)   Given the lengths of lines from the vertices of a triangle to the mid-points of the opposite sides, find its sides and angles.

(5)   A bag contains one counter, known to be either black or white. A white counter is put in, the bag is shaken, and a counter is drawn out, which proves to be white. What is now the chance of drawing a white counter?

Q1   Find the fallacy in this 'proof', attributed to Lewis Carroll, that every triangle has a pair of equal sides.

Data

In any $\triangle ABC$, the perpendicular bisector of BC meets the bisector of the angle BAC at P. PM, PN and PK are the perpendiculars to the sides BC, CA and AB.

Proof

(i) $\triangle PBM$ is congruent with $\triangle PCM$ (being right-angled triangles with PM common), and MB = MC. Hence PB = PC.

(ii) $\triangle PAK$ is congruent with $\triangle PAN$, having two pairs of equal angles, and AP is common to both. Hence AK = AN and PK = PN.

(iii) $\triangle PKB$ is congruent with $\triangle PNC$, being right-angled triangles with PK = PN and PB = PC. Hence KB = NC.

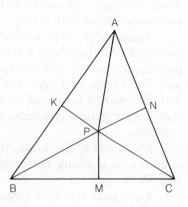

So AB = AK + KB = AN + NC = AC, showing that the sides AB and AC are equal.

Q.E.D.

There are a few references in his diary to his mathematical interests. In September 1897, he recorded:

27th   '*Dies notandus*. Discovered rule for dividing a number by 9 by mere addition and subtraction. I felt that there must be an analogous one for 11 . . . and proved my first rule by algebra after working about 9 hours.'

28th   'I have actually superseded the rules discovered yesterday. My new rules require to find the 9-remainder and the 11-remainder, which the others did not require: but the new ones are much the quickest.'

Q2   In 1890, he recorded in his diary this chance discovery about a pair of integers, x and y.

    a   If $x^2 + y^2$ is even, then its half is the sum of two squares.

    b $2(x^2 + y^2)$ is always the sum of two squares.

    c   Any number whose square is the sum of two squares is itself the sum of two squares.
        Can you prove these statements to be true or false?

Regrettably, Lewis Carroll's intention to publish a collection of games and puzzles as Volume 3 of *Curiosa Mathematica* was never realised, though a few problems have survived. Nevertheless, he was a pioneer in the field of recreational mathematics.

Q3   Prove algebraically that a number with five digits, a, b, c, d, e is

    a   a multiple of 9 when $a+b+c+d+e$ is a multiple of 9

    b   a multiple of 11 when $(a+c+e) - (b+d)$ is zero or a multiple of 11

Is it true that, however many digits a number has, it is a multiple of 9 when its digit sum is a multiple of 9, and that when the digit sum exceeds a multiple of 9 by n, where n is less than 9, then the remainder after division by 9 is n?

Dodgson published his discoveries about multiples of 9 and 11 in a mathematical periodical in 1897. He based his method of using only addition and subtraction to find the quotient and remainder after division of any number by 9 or 11 on the ideas in **Q3** above.

    There is an alternative method of finding the remainder after division by 11 that uses only subtraction, but the user must know that the subtraction of a negative number is equivalent to the addition of a positive number, i.e. that $-(-3) = +3$.

Example 1   Divide 1375 by 11
Subtract the first digit from the second. 1 from 3 leaves 2. Subtract this remainder from the third digit. 2 from 7 leaves 5. Subtract this remainder from the next digit. 5 from 5 leaves 0, which shows that 1375 is a multiple of 11.

Example 2   Divide 736 by 11
7 from 3 leaves -4, -4 from 6 leaves $+10$, which is the remainder after division by 11.

Q4   Use this method to find which of these numbers is a multiple of 11, and the remainder after division by 11 of those numbers which are not multiples of 11:

$$561, \ 651, \ 382, \ 1914, \ 15851, \ 70807, \ 567 \times 789$$

Q5   Investigate whether palindromic numbers with an even number of digits (e.g. 416614) are multiples of 11.

Q6   Explain why the method of continuous subtraction leads to the remainder after division by 11.

Lewis Carroll lived in the days of golden sovereigns, silver crowns, half-crowns, florins, shillings, sixpences and threepenny bits, and copper pennies, halfpennies and farthings. Here are some examples of the kind of coin puzzles that he invented.

Q7   A man paid a sovereign (20s) to a shopkeeper after purchasing goods to the value of 8s 10d. What is the least number of the above coins which the shopkeeper could give him in change?
If the man had wished to have coins that were all different from each other, could the shopkeeper have obliged him?

Q8   Mr Bookworm bought a number of novels by Mr Quackery at the same price, and paid the bookseller £7 7s 7d. Can you discover how many books he bought, and the price of each, if the number is known to be more than seven?

Q9   A housewife paid a greengrocer 7/6 for fruit and vegetables costing 6/7, and received 11d change. She wondered what change she would receive from 8/6 for goods worth 6/8, or from 10/6 for goods worth 6/10. What did she discover?
What is the difference between two amounts of shillings and pence when the numbers are interchanged (e.g. 11/3 and 3/11)?
Find the difference between m shillings n pence, and n shillings m pence $(m > n)$.

Lewis Carroll is credited with the discovery of this puzzle:

	£	s	d
Choose any sum of money less than £12, e.g.	10	17	5
Reverse the order of the figures	5	17	10
Find the difference	4	19	7
Again reverse the order of the figures	7	19	4
Add the last two amounts	12	18	11

If you choose your own amount of money, and perform the above calculation, what do you find?

Q10 Explain the above result.

Q11 Show that the sum of the numbers in the third row is always 30.

Q12 The amount in the final row above is 13d short of £13, and so it is exactly divisible by 13. What is the quotient? By what other prime number is it exactly divisible?

A similar result follows when a length less than 12 yards is chosen, given in yards, feet and inches, or when a weight less than 112 tons is given in tons, hundredweight and pounds.

Q13 What do you find in the case of

    a   lengths?

    b   weights?

Q14 There are 8 pints in a gallon. What do you find when you subtract y gallons x pints from x gallons y pints $(x > y)$, and then change the figures round and add the two quantities?
Is the final quantity exactly divisible by 7 and 9?

Q15 There are 1000 cm^3 in 1 litre. What do you find when these calculations are applied to x litres y cm^3?

Problems

100 years ago gold sovereigns and silver coins jingled in the pockets of eminent Victorians, such as Lewis Carroll, and girls like Alice could buy a packet of sweets for one penny. But at school arithmetic was more difficult than it is today, because of the complicated money system of pounds (£), shillings (s)

and pence (d), and children had to learn that

> 4 farthings (f) = 1 penny (d)
> 12 pennies   = 1 shilling (s)
> 20 shillings = 1 pound (£) = 1 sovereign

There were more coins: farthings (¼d), halfpence (½d), pennies (1d), which were made of copper, and threepenny bits (3d), sixpences (6d), shillings (1s), florins (2s) half-crowns (2s 6d), and crowns (5s), which were made of silver. Sovereigns (£1) and half-sovereigns (10s) were made of gold. For short £3 5s 4d was written £3/5/4.

1   When Alice emptied her money box, it contained 12 farthings, 15 halfpennies, 23 pennies, a threepenny bit, two shillings and one half-crown. How much more must she save so that she can buy two books costing 5/6 each?

2   Which is the largest sum of money: 1000d, 100s, 50 florins, 40 half-crowns or £4/16/8?

3   When postage for a letter was 1d, and postage for a post-card was ½d, how much would Lewis Carroll have had to pay for stamps on 32 letters and 17 postcards? How much change would he have received if he had offered two half-crowns in payment for the stamps?

4   Alice is 2 years older than Beatrice, and Beatrice is three years older than Caroline: the sum of their ages is 23 years. How old is each girl now, and what will be the sum of their ages in 23 years' time?

5   It is thought that the Mad Hatter was born on February 29th, 1860, and that the March Hare was born on March 13th, 1861. Some years later they met Alice one summer's day in Wonderland.

 The Mad Hatter claimed that he was an infant prodigy, as he was only 5¾ years old, having celebrated only five anniversaries of his birthday. He hoped to have his sixth birthday in the following year. Alice was good at mental arithmetic, and quickly calculated the age in years of the Mad Hatter and of the March Hare. How old were they?

As well as writing the imaginative stories of *Alice's Adventures in Wonderland* and *Through the Looking Glass*, Lewis Carroll invented word puzzles, one of which he called *Doublets*. For example, 'Increase TWO to TEN' by changing one letter at a time

> Solution: TWO — TOO — TON — TEN

This requires only two link words. Solve these puzzles, using not more than five link words.

6 *a* Stretch a YARD into a MILE.

 b Show that an ACE is represented by ONE.

 c Increase ZERO to a HALF.

 d Can COST and SALE be linked together?

 e Change speed from SLOW to FAST.

Lewis Carroll wrote a book called *The Game of Logic*. The game was played on a board with counters. The diagram below shows how a simpler board can be used to solve some problems.

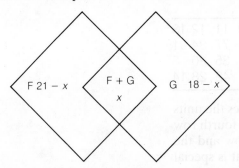 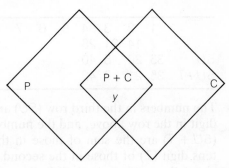

7 *a* In a class of 26 pupils, everyone must study either French or German, or both languages. If 21 pupils studied French and 18 studied German, how many studied both languages?

 b Everyone in the class must take either physics or chemistry or both. If 20 pupils study physics and 13 study chemistry, use the second diagram to find out how many pupils studied both these science subjects.

8 Find which of these patterned numbers is a multiple of 9, and what remainders are left by the others after division by 9:

12321, 123456789, 22122, 6767676, 135531, 123 × 321, 10201

9 Can you tell at a glance that 48 × 84 is not 4132?

10 Is 123456 + 654321 a multiple of 9?

11 Find which of these patterned numbers is a multiple of 11, and what remainders are left by the others after division by 11?

$123321, 50105, 365365, 10^2 + 1, 10^3 + 1, 10^4 + 1, 1010101$

12 Write down any number with four digits, and the number with the digits in the reverse order.

Is the difference between these two numbers always a multiple of 9, and their sum a multiple of 11?

13   Choose any whole number between 1 and 12, add 9, then multiply by 2, and subtract the number originally chosen.
If you add together the digits of the final number, what do you find?
Can you explain this?

14   Complete this multiplication table, in which the second row contains numbers 7 times those in the first row.

	1	2	3	4	5	6	7	8	9	10	11	12	13
	7	14	21	28							77	84	91
$5U$	35	20	5	40							35	20	5
$5U+T$	35	21	7	42							42	28	14

The numbers in the third row ($5U$) are five times the units digit in the row above, and the numbers in the fourth row ($5U + T$) are the sum of those in the third row and the tens digit (T) of those in the second row. What is special about the numbers in the fourth row?

15   Multiply by 7 any number greater than 13. Add five times the units digit to the number formed by the remaining digits, e.g. $29 \times 7 = 203$, $5 \times 3 + 20 = 35$.
Can you explain the result?

16   Which of these patterned numbers are multiples of 7? Test by adding five times the units digit to the remaining number.

161, 343, 1001, 5775, 13531, 32123, 12321

17   For what values of *a* and *b* are the patterned numbers

a   *abba* a multiple of 77

b   *ababa* a multiple of 7?

c   Find the smallest patterned number *abbba* that is a multiple of 7.

d   Is the number $aba = 7 \times m$ when $a+b = 7$ or 14?

18   To test whether a number with 3 digits is a multiple of 8, add the units digit (U) to twice the number formed by the other digits ($2T$). If $U + 2T$ is a multiple of 8, so is the original number.

Example Test 152

$U + 2T = 2 + 2 \times 15 = 32$, which is a multiple of 8. So 152 is a multiple of 8.

Use this test on these numbers to find out which are multiples of 8:

  204, 402, 192, 291, 216, 612, 704, 407

Can you explain why this test is valid?

If the number to be tested has more than 3 digits, why is it necessary to apply the test only to the last three digits?

If $U + 2T$ is not immediately recognisable as a multiple of 8, apply the test to it. Test 752, 752752, 1936 and 1020408.

19 There are similar tests to discover multiples of 12, 13, 17, and higher prime numbers. For example, if $10T + U$ is a multiple of 12, then $2T - U$ is also a multiple of 12.
Prove that this is true.
Use this test on 312, 3108 and 6804.

20 If $10T + U$ is a multiple of 13, is $T + 4U$ also a multiple of 13?
Which of these numbers are multiples of 13?

  52, 91, 104, 416, 13263952, 777777, 10012002

21 Try to find similar tests for divisibility by

a   17

b   19

c   23

d   29

e   31

f   89.

Hint: a similar test for divisibility by 9 is to investigate $T + U$. For example, for 432, $T = 43$ and $U = 2$. Hence $T + U = 43 + 2 = 45$, and $4 + 5 = 9$.

③ Magic squares

The magic square, in which the numbers from 1 to 9 are arranged in a square so that the sum of the three numbers in each row, column and diagonal is the same, has been known for over 4000 years. In a Chinese manuscript of about 2200 BC, the numbers are represented by patterns similar to those shown in Figure 1. The numbers can be placed in different positions, but 5 is always in the central cell, and the even numbers are in the corner cells.

Figure 2 shows the pattern formed by blacking out the odd numbers, and Figure 3 shows the Z-pattern formed by lines linking the cells containing the sequence of even numbers, 2, 4, 6, 8.

Q1 Is a similar pattern made by lines linking the cells containing the sequence of odd numbers 1, 3, 5, 7, 9?

Q2 What sequences are formed by the three numbers in the middle row, in the central column, and in each diagonal?

Figure 4 shows the V-pattern made by linking the cells containing the sequence 1, 2, 3. It is like two consecutive moves by a knight on a chess board.

Q3 Are similar patterns made by the sequences 7, 8, 9, and 1, 4, 7, and 3, 6, 9?

Q4

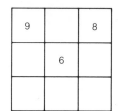
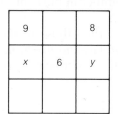

Recently a problem was set in an O-level mathematics examination paper about completing a 3-by-3 magic square in which only three numbers were shown, as in the above diagrams. It was suggested that the unknown number x

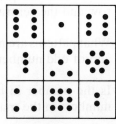

Figure 1

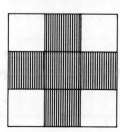

Figure 2

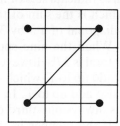

Figure 3

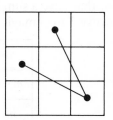

Figure 4

could be found by using the fact that the sum of the three numbers in the first column was the same as the sum of the three numbers in the diagonal containing 6 and 8. What is the value of x?

Similarly, y can be found by stating that the sum of the three numbers in the other diagonal equals the sum of the three numbers in the third column. What is the value of y? Having found x and y, the sum of the three numbers in the middle row can be found, and so all the other unknown numbers can be found.

Q5   Do you find sequences in the two diagonals, the middle row and the central column?

Q6   What patterns are made by the sequences of even numbers, and of odd numbers?

Q7   Is the number in the central cell the average of all nine numbers in the magic square?

You can make your own magic squares by using the patterns that appear in every 3-by-3 square.

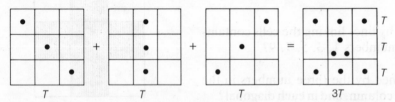

In the above diagram the three spots in the first three squares indicate sets of numbers whose sum is the same number T, which is the sum of the three numbers in each row, column and diagonal of a 3-by-3 magic square.

When the nine spots are transferred to a single square, their total is $3T$. However, the spots in the top and bottom rows each add up to T, which shows that the three spots in the central cell also add up to T. In other words, the number in the central cell is always one-third of T.

If the number in the central cell is m, then those in the diagonals must form sequences, $m-a$, m, $m+a$, and $m-b$, m, $m+b$, that have a sum of $3m = T$. Hence the algebraic pattern for every 3-by-3 magic square is

$m+a$	$m-a-b$	$m+b$
$m-a+b$	m	$m+a-b$
$m-b$	$m+a+b$	$m-a$

where m, a, b are any numbers, integral or fractional.

Q8 Show that, if $a = 2b$, two cells will contain the same
number, $m+b$, and two cells will contain the number $m-b$.
To avoid repeated numbers in a magic square, $a \neq 2b$
and $b \neq 2a$ are necessary, and, to avoid zero or negative
numbers, m must exceed $a + b$. The smallest set of positive
integers fulfilling these conditions is $m = 5$, $a = 3$, $b = 1$,
and these produce the Chinese magic square, made with
the numbers from 1 to 9.

Q9 What special magic square is made by putting $m = 9$,
$a = 6$, $b = 2$?
Do multiples of 3 make a pattern?
Do the prime numbers, 1, 3, 5, 7, etc. form a symmetrical
pattern?

Q10 What special magic square is made by putting $m = 37$,
$a = 30$, $b = 6$?
Do the numbers containing the numeral 3 form a symmetrical pattern?

Q11 Is it true that, in every 3-by-3 magic square, any set of
three numbers linked by the V-shaped pattern of Figure
4 form a sequence?

Q12 In the Chinese magic square is a symmetrical pattern
formed by linking cells containing the sequence of the first
nine numbers.

Q13

	1	
	7	

	1	
	13	
	7	

$2m-7$	1	
	m	
		7

Complete the above magic square by putting any number
greater than 7 in the central cell: you will find that one
cell will always contain the number 13.
Explain why this is so.
What happens when 13 is put in the central cell?
Complete the algebraic magic square when m is the
number in the central cell.

Problems

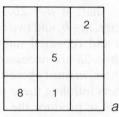

a

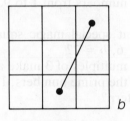

b

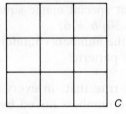

c

1   Complete the Chinese magic square (a) so that the sum of the three numbers in each row, column and diagonal is the same.

Diagram (b) shows the lines joining the cells containing the numbers 1 and 2 in the Chinese magic square: add the line joining the cells containing the numbers 2 and 3.

Is the diagonal containing 2, 5, 8 a line of symmetry of the pattern made by the lines joining the sequence 1, 2, 3?

Next, add to the diagram (b) the lines linking the sequences 7, 8, 9, and 3, 6, 9, and 1, 4, 7. Is the result a pattern with four lines of symmetry?

Copy the empty square (c), and draw the lines linking the four sequences 4, 5, 6, and 3, 5, 7, and 2, 5, 8, and 1, 5, 9. Is the result a pattern in which each straight line is a line of symmetry?

2   Draw a 3-by-3 square, and fill it with numbers that are double those in the cells of the Chinese magic square. Is the result a magic square?

If you now draw a 3-by-3 square in which each number is 1 less than the corresponding number in the previous square, what is special about the resulting square?

Fill squares with the final figures (the units digits) of the numbers in each of these magic squares. Do the lines joining cells containing the same pair of numbers form a symmetrical pattern?

3

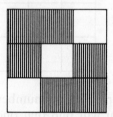

The cells of a 3-by-3 square have been filled with the numbers 1, 2, 3.

Is it a magic square?

Does each row, column and diagonal contain the numbers 1, 2 and 3?

If the cells containing odd numbers are black, and those containing even numbers are white, the above black and white pattern is made: how many lines of symmetry has it?

4

	2	
	6	
		3

Copy this magic square and complete it so that the sum of the three numbers in each row, column and diagonal is 18.
Copy the empty square and draw the black and white pattern made by odd and even numbers in the completed magic square.

5 Copy and complete this magic square. You will find that it contains the first nine odd numbers, and so would have an all black odd and even pattern but, if cells containing multiples of 3 are black and the others white, what pattern is formed?
It also contains the first seven prime numbers: if they are black and composite (non-prime) numbers are white, is the resulting pattern symmetrical?
If so, how many lines of symmetry does it have?

11	13	
	9	
		7

6

6	8	
7		

		10
5		
6		

x	$x+1$	
	$x+2$	
		$x+4$

Complete the above magic squares so that the sum of the three numbers in each row, column and diagonal is 24?

7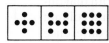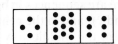

What is the sum of the three numbers on each of these strips?
On which strip do the numbers form a sequence?
This strip is the middle row of a magic square: arrange the three strips so as to form the complete magic square (note: one or two strips could be rotated, so that the order of numbers is reversed).

8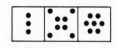

A magic square has been cut into three pieces: what is the sum of the three numbers in the straight strip above?
What does this show is the number in the central cell?
Using the strip as the bottom row, fit the two corner pieces onto it so as to complete the magic square.
What are the differences between the numbers in the sequences shown in the middle row, the central column and the two diagonals?

9 In this algebraic magic square, what is the sum of the numbers in each row, column and diagonal?
Find the magic squares when

$2a + 3b$	$a + b$	$3a + 2b$
$3a + b$	$2a + 2b$	$a + 3b$
$a + 2b$	$3a + 3b$	$2a + b$

a $a = 1, b = 0$

b $a = 1, b = 3$

c $a = 2, b = 3$

d $a = 3, b = -1$

e $a = 2 = 2b$

f $b = 2a.$

Choose your own numbers for a and b.
Do any of these magic squares contain a set of nine consecutive numbers?
Is it true that when $b = 2a$ (or $a = 2b$) the magic square contains repeated numbers?

10 Every 3-by-3 magic square can be made by putting numbers for m, x and y in these algebraic formulae. All the numbers in the square will be different unless $x = 2y$ or $y = 2x$.
All the numbers will be positive if m is greater than $x + y$.
This square shows that there are sequences in both diagonals (with differences of x and y), and in the central column (difference of $x + y$), and in the middle row (difference of $x - y$).

$m + y$	$m - x - y$	$m + x$
$m + x - y$	m	$m - x + y$
$m - x$	$m + x + y$	$m - y$

What special magic squares are made by putting

a $m = 5, x = 1, y = 3$

b $m = 9, x = 2, y = 6$

c $m = 59, x = 12, y = 42$?

Make your own magic squares by choosing numbers for m, x and y.
What values of m, x, y produce this magic square?
Find the pattern for the sequence 5, 7, 9, 11, 13, 15, 17.

17	1	15
9	11	13
7	21	5

4 Pythagoras and his theorem

It is not known whether Pythagoras, the Greek mathematician born *circa* 570 BC, ever produced a general geometric proof of the theorem that bears his name, that the area of the square on the hypotenuse of any right-angled triangle is equal to the sum of the areas of the squares on its two other sides.

The theoretical proof given by Euclid in Book I of his *Elements* as Theorem 47 in the logical sequence of propositions based upon axioms and definitions is still reproduced in school textbooks on geometry, although a shorter proof can easily be deduced from a theorem on similar triangles in Book VI of the *Elements*.

Q1 a, b, c are the lengths of the sides of $\triangle ABC$ (Figure 1), which is right-angled at C. It is required to prove that $c^2 = a^2 + b^2$.

Draw CN perpendicular to AB, and show that it divides $\triangle ABC$ into two triangles that are similar to $\triangle ABC$.

By writing down the equal ratios of pairs of corresponding sides, show that $a^2 = cx$ and $b^2 = c^2 - cx$, and deduce that $a^2 + b^2 = c^2$.

Q2 Prove Pythagoras' theorem by using the fact that the ratio of the areas of similar shapes is the square of the ratio of the lengths of their corresponding sides.

Q3 Use Figure 2 to demonstrate that $a^2 + b^2 = c^2$.

This is one of many proofs by dissection of the squares on the sides a and b of the $\triangle ABC$, right-angled at C, so that the pieces fit exactly into the square on the hypotenuse, c.

A diagram in a Chinese manuscript, probably written over 4000 years ago, indicates that it was already known that $3^2 + 4^2 = 5^2$, and that a triangle with sides proportional to (3, 4, 5) was right-angled. Other sets of three numbers (a, b, c) such that $a^2 + b^2 = c^2$ were known before the time of Pythagoras, but he probably deserves the credit for discovering a method for finding an infinite series of such sets.

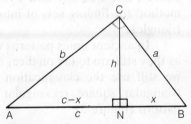

Figure 1 A right-angled triangle

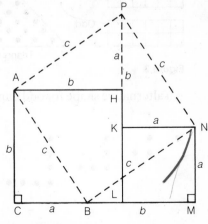

Figure 2 Proof of Pythagoras' theorem

Using Arabic numerals his method is as follows:

choose any odd number (greater than 1), e.g. 5

its square will also be an odd number, 25

this odd number is the sum of two consecutive numbers, 12 + 13

then (5, 12, 13) are proportional to the lengths of the sides of a right-angled triangle, since $5^2 + 12^2 = 13^2$

To verify this, factorise $13^2 - 12^2$.

Q4 Using algebra, if $a = 2n + 1$, find b and c in terms of n. Is it true that b is always four times a triangular number?

Q5 Using the formulae for (a, b, c) that you have found, what are a and b when $c = 1^2 + 12^2$?

Q6 Find x when $a = 2x + 1$, $b = 3x + 1$, $c = 4x + 1$.

When we recollect that the Greek mathematicians at that time had no numerals, but used the letters of the Greek alphabet to record numbers and made arithmetical calculations on an abacus, one wonders how Pythagoras was able to discover his method for finding sets of integers that produced right-angled triangles.

In ancient times patterns were used to represent numbers, as they still are today on dice, dominoes and playing cards, and we still use the classification of numbers — odd and even, triangular, square, rectangular — according to the shape of the pattern (Figure 3).

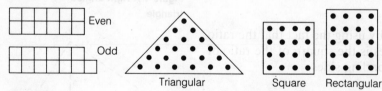

Figure 3

An alternative shape for odd numbers was the 'gnomon':

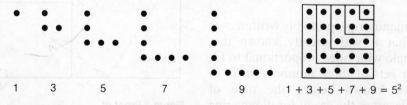

This shape led to the discovery that the sum of consecutive odd numbers is always a square number:

$$1 = 1^2$$
$$1 + 3 = 4 = 2^2$$
$$1 + 3 + 5 = 9 = 3^2$$
$$1 + 3 + 5 + 7 = 16 = 4^2$$
$$(1 + 3 + 5 + 7) + 9 = 25 = 5^2$$

This last result can be interpreted as

$$4^2 + 9 = 4^2 + 3^2 = 5^2$$

showing that (3, 4, 5) satisfies, $a^2 + b^2 = c^2$.

Since the square of the odd number 5 is $25 = 12 + 13$, the gnomon for 25 will fit round the square number, 12^2, to make the next square number, 13^2, and so $5^2 + 12^2 = 13^2$ (Figure 4). Similarly, $7^2 = 49 = 24 + 25$, and so the gnomon for 7^2 will fit round the square number 24^2 to make the next square number 25^2, so that $7^2 + 24^2 = 25^2$.

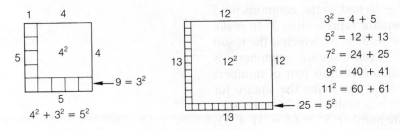

$$3^2 = 4 + 5$$
$$5^2 = 12 + 13$$
$$7^2 = 24 + 25$$
$$9^2 = 40 + 41$$
$$11^2 = 60 + 61$$

Figure 4

My conjecture is that Pythagoras realised that this could be continued and that the gnomon for the square of any odd number, being the sum of two consecutive numbers, could be fitted round the square representing the square of the first to make the square of the second. If this is so, he had found a method for producing an infinite series of sets of numbers (*a, b, c*) that satisfy $a^2 + b^2 = c^2$ by using number patterns.

There are other methods for finding more sets of integers (*a, b, c*), one of which is given in the writings of the Greek philosopher Plato (*circa* 400 BC). In modern notation, if *a* is any even number, $2m$, then $b = m^2 - 1$, $c = m^2 + 1$.

Q7 Verify the Platonic formula when $m = 2, 3, 4$, or 5.
Which of these produce (*a, b, c*) sets that are multiples of those discovered by the Pythagorean method?

Q8 When *m* is an odd number, $2n + 1$, what is special about the resulting (*a, b, c*) set?

My conjecture is that Plato, or a contemporary mathematician, discovered this method from the same pattern that Pythagoras had used. It can be shown that every multiple of 4 can be expressed as the sum of two consecutive odd numbers, i.e. $4m = (2m - 1) + (2m + 1)$. Since the square of any even number is a multiple of 4, it can be expressed as the sum of two consecutive odd numbers, and these can be represented by two gnomons that fit round a square (Figure 5).

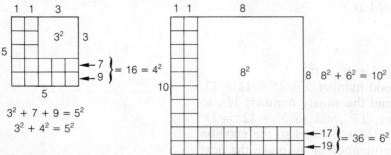

$3^2 + 7 + 9 = 5^2$
$3^2 + 4^2 = 5^2$

$8^2 + 6^2 = 10^2$

Figure 5

For example, $4^2 = 16 = 7 + 9$, and so the gnomons for 7 and 9 can be fitted round the square representing 3^2 to make the square representing 5^2, i.e. $4^2 + 3^2 = 5^2$, which is the result already known. The next even square number is $6^2 = 36 = 17 + 19$, and the gnomons for this pair of numbers can be fitted round the square for 8^2, to make the square for 10^2, so that $6^2 + 8^2 = 10^2$, which is a multiple of $3^2 + 4^2 = 5^2$. But, if we try the next even square number, $8^2 = 64 = 31 + 33$, we find that $8^2 + 15^2 = 17^2$ — a new result.

The Platonic formula provides an infinite series of sets for (a, b, c) in which $c - b = 2$, just as in the Pythagorean series $c - b = 1$. The general formula for integral solutions to $a^2 + b^2 = c^2$ was not discovered until centuries later, after algebra had been developed, but the Greeks could have derived it from Plato's formulae, $a = 2m, b = m^2 - 1, c = m^2 + 1$, by putting a fraction m/n in place of m, so that

$$a = 2m/n$$
$$b = (m^2 - n^2)/n^2$$
$$c = (m^2 + n^2)/n^2$$

and multiplying by n^2, $a = 2mn, b = m^2 - n^2, c = m^2 + n^2$, which is the general formula, valid for integral values of m and n.

Q9 Find (a, b, c) when $m = 5, n = 2$.
Is it true that $a = b - 1$?

Q10 Euclid (*circa* 300 BC) is credited with finding a proof that the square root of 2 cannot be a rational fraction m/n. Using algebra can you prove that there are no integers m and n such that $m^2 = 2n^2$?

Q11 Can you see why the square root of 2 lies between 29/21 and 29/20?

Problems

1

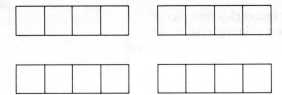

The four rectangles shown above can be fitted together to form a 4-by-4 square.

Fit them onto the 3-by-3 square to show that $3^2 + 4^2 = 5^2$.

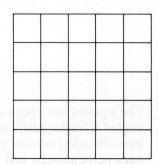

2 If you remove the 3-by-3 square from the top right-hand corner of this 5-by-5 square an L-shaped piece remains, which can then be cut into pieces to form a 4-by-4 square.

What is the least number of pieces required to do this?

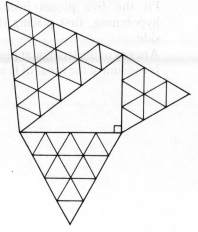

3 Equilateral triangles have been drawn on the sides of a (3, 4, 5) right-angled triangle.

How many small triangles are in each of the larger equilateral triangles?

Discover how to dissect the largest equilateral triangle into four pieces that can be fitted together to make the two other triangles.

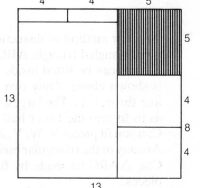

4 A 5-by-5 square has been removed from a 13-by-13 square, and the remaining L-shaped piece has been cut into five rectangular pieces.

Can you fit them together to make another square?

What is the number x that satisfies $5^2 + x^2 = 13^2$.

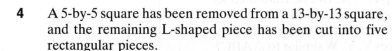

5   A 7-by-7 square has been removed from a 25-by-25 square, and the remaining piece has been cut into three rectangles, one 18-by-24, another 7-by-18, and the narrow strip 1-by-18.

Discover how to cut the two smaller rectangles into pieces which can be fitted on to the largest rectangle so as to form a square.

What is y when $y^2 + 7^2 = 25^2$?

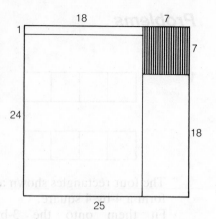

6   The squares have been drawn on the three sides of right-angled triangle ABC, and the two smaller squares have been dissected into five pieces marked P, Q, R, S, T, along lines perpendicular and parallel to the hypotenuse AB.

Fit the five pieces inside the empty square on the hypotenuse, first placing the piece P along its left-hand side.

Are any of the triangular pieces Q, S, T, similar to $\triangle$ABC?

Is the sum of the areas of R and S equal to the area of T?

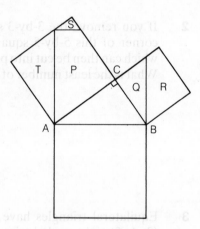

7   Another method of dissecting the squares on two sides of a right-angled triangle ABC into five pieces V, W, X, Y, Z, that can be fitted inside the square on the hypotenuse is shown above. Only two cuts are needed, one along a line through C. The largest piece, X, can be translated so as to fit into the lower half of the square on AB.

Can you fit pieces V, W, Y, Z into the remaining space?

Are any of the triangular pieces V, Y, W similar to $\triangle$ABC?

Can $\triangle$ABC be made by fitting together two of the five pieces?

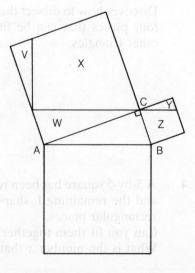

8 *a* △ABC is right-angled at C, and CN is perpendicular to the hypotenuse AB.
Explain why △CBN and △ACN are similar to △ABC, and why the ratio of their corresponding sides is $a{:}b{:}c$.

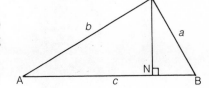

b Why is the ratio of the areas of these triangles $a^2{:}b^2{:}c^2$?

c Deduce that $a^2 + b^2 = c^2$.

9

n	10	11	12	13	14	15	16	17	18	19	20	21
n^2	100	121	144									
$2n+1$	21	23	25									

In this table the squares of 10, 11, 12 are shown in the second row of numbers, and in the third row are shown the differences between consecutive pairs of square numbers, $(n + 1)^2 - n^2 = 2n + 1$, which form the sequence of odd numbers.

By continuing this sequence the corresponding square numbers can easily be found, $100 + 21 = 121$, $121 + 23 = 144$, $144 + 25 = ?$

When you have completed this table use it to find x, y, z, etc. when $8^2 + 15^2 = x^2$, $9^2 + 12^2 = y^2$, $12^2 + 16^2 = z^2$, $w^2 + 21^2 = 29^2$, $u^2 + 20^2 = 25^2$, $v^2 + 24^2 = 26^2$, $t^2 + 40^2 = 41^2$, $s^2 + 35^2 = 37^2$.

Show that 365 is the sum of three consecutive square numbers, and also the sum of the next two consecutive square numbers.
(*Hint*: use $a^2 - b^2 = (a-b)(a+b)$ whenever possible.)

10 Can you find positive values for x, y and z such that the triangles with sides

a x, $x - 1$, $x + 1$

b y, $2y - 1$, $2y + 1$

c $z - 4$, $z - 5$, $z + 4$

are right-angled?

11 Find two positive values of x such that the triangle with sides x, $2x + 2$, $3x - 2$ is right-angled.
Are the two possible triangles similar?

12 Find a right-angled triangle whose perimeter is 24 cm, and whose hypotenuse is 4 cm less than the sum of the two other sides.
Is its area more or less than that of a square of sides 5 cm?

8   **a** $\triangle ABC$ is right-angled at C, and CN is perpendicular to the hypotenuse AB.

Explain why $\triangle CBN$ and $\triangle ACN$ are similar to $\triangle ABC$, and why the ratio of their corresponding sides is $a:b:c$.

   b   Why is the ratio of the areas of these triangles $a^2:b^2:c^2$?

   c   Deduce that $a^2 + b^2 = c^2$.

9

n	10	11	12	13	14	15	16	17	18	19	20	21
n^2	100	121	144									
$2n+1$	21	23	25									

In this table the squares of 10, 11, 12 are shown in the second row of numbers, and in the third row are shown the differences between consecutive pairs of square numbers, $(n + 1)^2 - n^2 = 2n + 1$, which form the sequence of odd numbers.

By continuing this sequence the corresponding square numbers can easily be found, $100 + 21 = 121$, $121 + 23 = 144$, $144 + 25 = 9$.

When you have completed this table use it to find x, y, z, etc. when $8^2 + 15^2 = x^2$, $9^2 + 12^2 = y^2$, $12^2 + 16^2 = z^2$, $x^2 + 21^2 = 29^2$, $v^2 + 20^2 = 25^2$, $y^2 + 24^2 = 26^2$, $t^2 + 40^2 = 41^2$, $s^2 + 35^2 = 37^2$.

Show that 365 is the sum of three consecutive square numbers, and also the sum of the next two consecutive square numbers.

(Hint: use $a^2 - b^2 = (a-b)(a+b)$ whenever possible.)

10   Can you find positive values for x, y and z such that the triangles with sides

   a x, $x - 1$, $x + 1$

   b y, $2y - 1$, $2y + 1$

   c $z - 4$, $z - 5$, $z + 4$

are right-angled?

11   Find two positive values of x such that the triangle with sides x, $2x + 2$, $3x - 2$ is right-angled.
Are the two possible triangles similar?

12   Find a right-angled triangle whose perimeter is 24 cm, and whose hypotenuse is 1 cm less than the sum of the two other sides.
Is its area more or less than that of a square of sides 5 cm?

⑤ *Jigsaw puzzles*

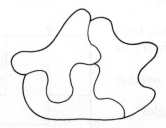

Jigsaw puzzles are of interest to most children and to some adults, as a recent competitive game on television recently showed. The skill required is partly an ability to match colours and partly to match curved shapes.

Dissections of geometrical shapes can produce jigsaw puzzles with straight-edged pieces that familiarise children with the language and ideas of elementary geometry.

Q1 A rectangle can be dissected into four identical right-angled triangles.
How many different symmetrical shapes can you make with the four pieces by fitting equal edges together?

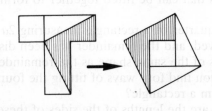

Q2 Dissect the six tetrominoes, made with four equal squares, into two pieces that can be fitted together to form a square.
Which of the shapes can be dissected in

a one way only

b two different ways?

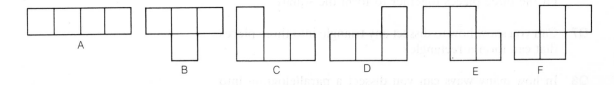

Q3

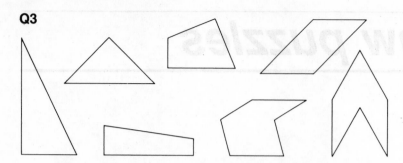

Can you see how to dissect each of these shapes into two pieces that can be fitted together to form a square?

Q4 One-quarter of a rectangle measuring 2*a* by 2*b* has been removed, and the remainder has been dissected into four pieces of the same shape as the remainder.
Can you find four ways of fitting the four pieces together to form a rectangle?
What are the lengths of the sides of these rectangles?

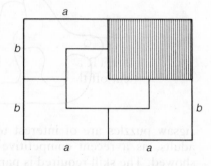

Q5 A rectangle ABCD has been dissected into three pieces by cuts along AX and BY perpendicular to AX, where X is any point between C and D.
Can you fit the three pieces together to form another rectangle?
What special cases arise when

a   AX = AB

b   AX = BY?

Can you deduce a method for dissecting a rectangle into pieces that can form a square?

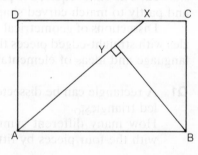

Q6 Another method for dissecting a rectangle into pieces that can form a square is to calculate (or find by geometrical construction) the length of the side of the square whose area is the same as that of the rectangle. Then mark points P in AB, and Q in CD, such that PB and DQ are equal in length to the side of the square. QR is then drawn at right-angles to CD.
Fit the three pieces together to form the square.

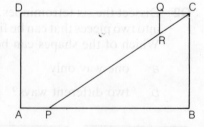

Q7 Can you show how to dissect any triangle into three pieces that can form a rectangle?

Q8 In how many ways can you dissect a parallelogram into two pieces that can form a rectangle?

Q9 Can you show how to dissect any quadrilateral into four
pieces that can form a parallelogram?

Q10 A regular pentagon can be dissected into six pieces that
form a square by first cutting off an isosceles triangle RST
and placing it with the side SR along TP.

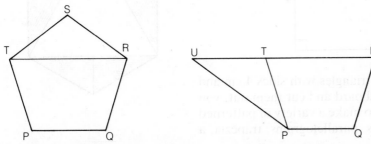

Why is UTR a straight line, and PQRU a trapezium?
Next cut off the triangle UVM, where M is the mid-point
of PU, and MV is parallel to QR, and placing it with UM
along PM.

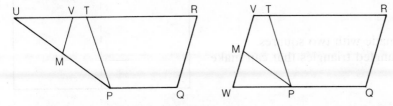

Do V, M, W lie on a straight line?
Why does VWQR form a parallelogram?
This parallelogram can be dissected into six pieces that
form a square by cutting along the lines VX and RY, at
right-angles to each other, where VX = RY is the length
of the side of the square whose area equals that of the
parallelogram VWQR.
The result is the dissection of the pentagon shown below:
can you fit the pieces together to form a square?

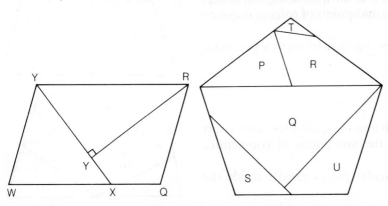

Problems

1

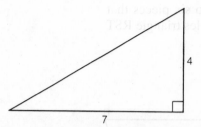

If you draw six right-angled triangles with sides 4 cm and 7 cm long on a piece of cardboard and cut them out, you can use some or all of them to make a variety of patterned shapes – triangles, rectangles, parallelograms, trapezia, a rhombus, etc.
The right-angled triangle is approximately one-half of an equilateral triangle.
Can you make a hollow hexagon with 7 cm sides, enclosing a hexagon with 4 cm sides?

2   Cut out a domino shape, made with two squares.
Dissect it into three right-angled triangles that can make a square.

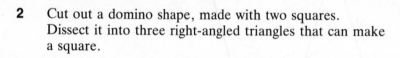

3   Cut out a rhombus with four equal sides and dissect along its diagonals of different lengths.
How many quadrilateral shapes can you make with the four pieces?

4   Cut out a quadrilateral with four unequal sides, and dissect it along the lines joining the mid-points of pairs of opposite sides.
Can you fit the four pieces together to form a parallelogram?

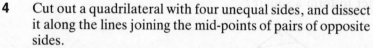

5   Cut out a quadrilateral with four unequal sides, and dissect it along the lines joining the mid-points of consecutive sides.
Can you fit the four triangular pieces exactly inside the remaining quadrilateral?

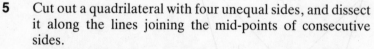

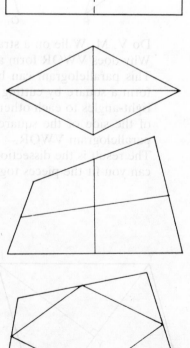

6 Dissect any parallelogram along a diagonal and a line perpendicular to it through a corner.
Can you fit the three triangular pieces together to form a rectangle?

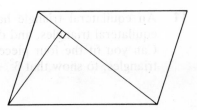

7 The diagram shows one way of dissecting a trapezium into two parts that can form a parallelogram.
Can you find two other ways of doing this?

8 Cut any triangle into three pieces along the lines KN and ML, where K, M, N are mid-points of the sides and ML is perpendicular to KN.
How many different shapes can you make by fitting the pieces together?

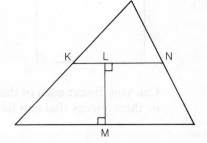

9 Can you dissect the 2-by-2 square into four pieces that fit round the single square to form a larger square?

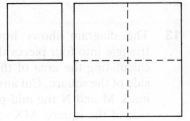

10

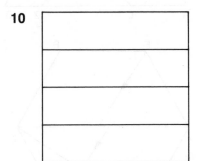

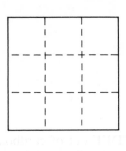

A 4-by-4 square has been cut into four equal rectangles.
Can you fit them round the 3-by-3 square so as to make a 5-by-5 square?

11   An equilateral triangle has been divided into 25 small equilateral triangles, and dissected into four pieces. Can you fit the four pieces together to form equilateral triangles, to show that $3^2 + 4^2 = 5^2$?

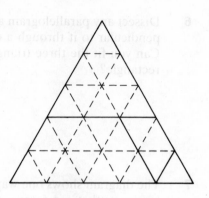

12

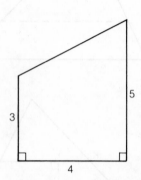

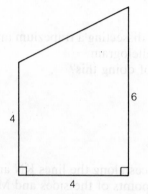

Can you dissect each of the right-angled trapezia into two or three pieces that can form a square?

13   The diagram shows how to dissect any acute-angled triangle into four pieces that can form a square, after first calculating the area of the triangle and the length of the side of the square. Cut any triangle ABC out of cardboard, mark M and N the mid-points of AC and BC. NL is the side of the square. MX and YZ are perpendicular to NL, and NY = XL.

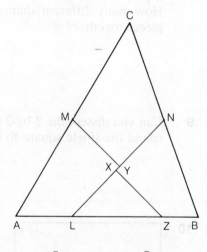

14   Cut a regular hexagon ABCDEF out of cardboard, and dissect it into five pieces along the diagonal AD, FQ (the side of the square (equal to approximately 6AB/5), mark AR = QD, and cut along RS parallel to FQ.
Fit the five pieces together to form a square.

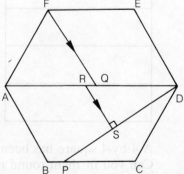

15 The eight-pointed 'star' is made by a white square overlapping an equal black square. Cut off the four black triangles. Can you dissect the white square into four pieces that make a square around the four black pieces?

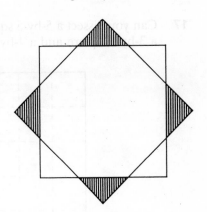

16 The diagrams below show 11 different shapes of pentominoes made with five equal squares.

The first three have been dissected into four parts: can you fit each of them together to form a square?

Can you discover how to dissect the shape D into three pieces that form a square?

The shape K can be dissected into five pieces that form a square, but each of the others requires only three or four pieces.

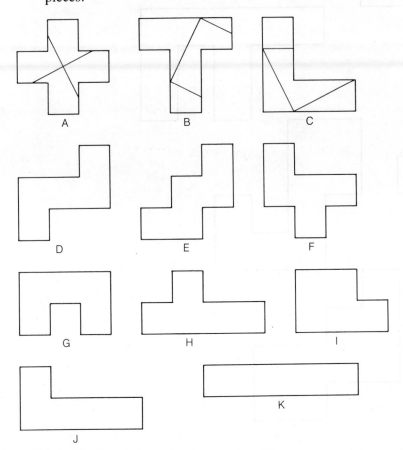

17   Can you dissect a 5-by-5 square into four pieces that make
a 3-by-3 square and a 4-by-4 square?

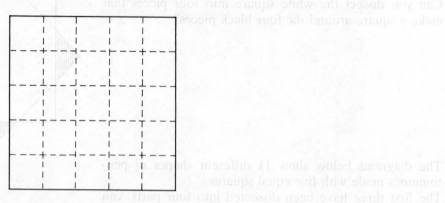

18   Can you dissect each of these shapes into two pieces that
can be fitted together to make 3-by-3 squares?

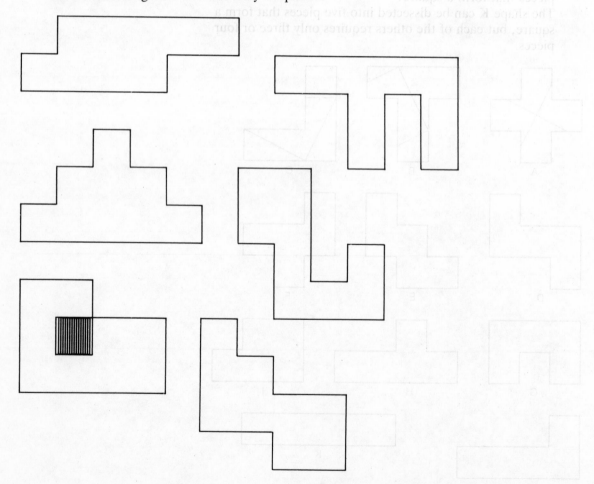

19   *a*   The four right-angled triangles made by cutting a square along its diagonals can be fitted round another square to make a larger square.
If the area of the first square is one square unit, what is the area of the larger square?

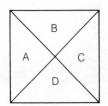

b   Can you dissect a one unit square into four equal triangles of a different shape, and fit them together to make a larger square that forms a border to a smaller square?
What is the area of each square?

c   Can you dissect a one unit square into four equal quadrilaterals in five different ways?

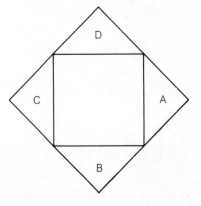

(i)   Four rectangles that can make a larger square that forms a border to a smaller square.
What is the area of each square?

(ii)   Four squares that can make all the shapes of tetrominoes.

(iii)   Four trapezia that can form a parallelogram.

(iv)   Four cyclic quadrilaterals that can form a border to a square.

(v)   Four trapezia that can form a hexagon.

20   What symmetrical shapes can you make by fitting together

a   the four pieces A, B, C, D

b   P, Q, R, S?

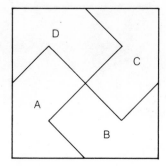

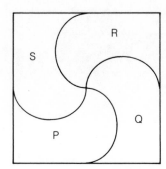

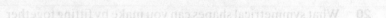

6 Prime numbers

The great Greek mathematicians, such as Pythagoras and Euclid, who laid the theoretical foundations of arithmetic and geometry, separated the natural numbers into two classes — prime numbers and composite numbers. They used axioms, definitions and logic.

A prime number was defined as being divisible exactly only by one and itself, whereas a composite number was the product of two factors less than itself.

Composite numbers can be represented by square or rectangular patterns: for example, $4 = 2 \times 2$ has the pattern

```
o   o
o   o
```

and $12 = 2 \times 6 = 3 \times 4$ has the two rectangular patterns

```
o   o   o   o   o   o
o   o   o   o   o   o
```

and

```
o   o   o   o
o   o   o   o
o   o   o   o
```

in which the length and breadth indicate the pair of factors.

Thus the first seven prime numbers are 1, 2, 3, 5, 7, 11, 13. 2 is the only even prime number; the others are all odd.

Q1 Prove algebraically that all prime numbers greater than 3 are either one more or one less than a multiple of 6.

Q2 If you complete this table showing the squares of seven consecutive prime numbers, and the remainders after division by 10 and by 24, what do you discover?

p	5	7	11	13	17	19	23
p^2	25	49					
R(10)	5	9					
R(24)	1						

Q3 If two prime numbers greater than 3 differ by 2, what is special about their product plus one?

About 250 BC Eratosthenes, the mathematician, astronomer and librarian at Alexandria University, made the first calculation of the radius of the earth, though he achieved greater fame by his invention of a method of separating prime and composite numbers, known as the sieve of Eratosthenes.

If you write down the sequence of natural numbers

$$1, 2, 3, 4, 5, 6, 7, 8, 9, 10, 11, 12, 13, 14, 15, 16, 17, \ldots$$

and delete every second number after 2, you will have 'sieved out' all the composite even numbers, 4, 6, 8, etc. Next delete every third number after 3, and you will have removed composite numbers that are multiples of 3. Then delete every fifth number after 5, every seventh number after 7, every eleventh number after 11, every thirteenth number after 13, and you will have left only the prime numbers less than $289 = 17^2$.

A modern kind of sieve uses patterns to remove composite numbers quickly from a table of odd numbers. A small model of this kind shows odd numbers less than 50:

1	3	5	7	9
11	13	15	17	19
21	23	25	27	29
31	33	35	37	39
41	43	45	47	49

Multiples of 3 can be sieved out easily as they all appear in diagonal lines, and multiples of 5 lie in the central column. The only composite number remaining is 49, the square of the next prime number, 7.

1	3	5	7	9	11	13	15	17	19	21	23	25	27	29
31	33	35	37	39	41	43	45	47	49	51	53	55	57	59
61	63	65	67	69	71	73	75	77	79	81	83	85	87	89
91	93	95	97	99	101	103	105	107	109	111	113	115	117	119

In this table of the first 60 odd numbers, multiples of 5 still appear in columns: where are all multiples of 3? Multiples of

7 lie on diagonals — like a bishop's move on a chess board — whilst multiples of 13 and 17 make knight's move patterns:

```
 o   o   o   o   o   o  13   o  17   o   o   o   o   o
 o   o   o   o  39   o   o   o   o   o  51   o   o   o
 o   o  65   o   o   o   o   o   o   o   o   o  85   o   o
91   o   o   o   o   o   o   o   o   o   o   o   o   o  119
```

The pattern formed by multiples of 11 is not so obvious, but it can be described as 'move one down and then four to the left (or seven to the right)'.

Multiples of all prime numbers form patterns on the table: for example, multiples of 29, and multiples of 31, form knight's move patterns. Multiples of 19 and 23 make less obvious patterns but, on a table showing odd numbers less than 1000, one need delete only $361 = 19^2$, $529 = 23^2$ and $961 = 31^2$ after 'sieving out' multiples of primes from 3 to 17.

1	3	5	7	11	13	17	19	23	29
1	3	5	7	11	13	17	19	23	29
31			37	41	43	47		53	59
61			67	71	73		79	83	89
			97	101	103	107	109	113	
			127	131		137	139		149
151			157		163	167		173	179
181				191	193	197	199		
211					223	227	229	233	239
241				251		257		263	269
271			277	281	283			293	
			307	311	313	317			
331			337			347	349	353	359
			367		373		379	383	389
			397	401			409		419
421				431	433		439	443	449
			457	461	463	467			479
			487	491			499	503	509
				521	523				
541			547			557		563	569
571			577			587		593	599
601			607		613	617	619		
631				641	643	647		653	659
661					673	677		683	
691				701			709		719

Q4 What do you discover by completing this table showing the values of $m = n^2 - n + 11$ from $n = 1$ to $n = 13$?

n	1	2	3	4	5	6	7	8	9	10	11	12	13
n^2	1	4	9	16									
$n^2 - n$	0	2	6										
m	11	13											

The English mathematician Barlow is credited with finding that a finite sequence of prime numbers is produced by the formula $n^2 - n + 17$, and Euler made a similar discovery about the formula $n^2 - n + 41$.

Q5 How many prime numbers are produced by each of the above formulae by putting $n = 1, 2, 3$ etc.?

Q6 Why is it impossible to find an algebraic formula that produces prime numbers for every value of n?

Q7 What is the smallest value of n that produces a composite number from the formula $3n^2 - 3n + 1$?
What is the smallest square number produced by this formula?

Q8 The author has found several quadratic formulae such as $4n^2 + 1$, that produce a sequence of prime numbers.
Can you find any?

Q9 Investigate formulae $2n^2 + p$, where p is any prime number greater than 3, for values of n from zero upwards.
What do you discover?
(Barlow discovered the formula $2n^2 + 29$.)

Q10 How many prime numbers are produced by the formulae $4n^2 + 37$ and $6n^2 + 7$?

Q11 Other formulae worth investigating are

$5n^2 - 5n + 1$	$7n^2 - 7n + 17$
$2n^2 - 2n + 7$	$2n^2 - 2n + 19$
$3n^2 - 3n + 11$	$3n^2 - 3n + 23$
$5n^2 - 5n + 13$	$4n^2 - 164n + 1523$

Despite the efforts of 19th and 20th century mathematicians who were interested in the theory of numbers, no one has yet succeeded in proving the conjecture made by the Russian Goldbach that all even numbers can be expressed as the sum of two prime numbers.

If the number of ways in which an even number $2n$ can be expressed as the sum of two prime numbers by the symbol $P(2n)$, then, since $10 = 3 + 7 = 5 + 5$, $P(10) = 2$.

Q12 What do you discover by completing this table?

$2n$	$P(2n)$
$2 = 1 + 1$	1
$4 = 1 + 3 = 2 + 2$	2
$6 = 1 + 5 =$	
$8 =$	
$10 = 3 + 7 = 5 + 5$	2
$12 =$	
$14 =$	
$16 =$	
$18 =$	
$20 = \quad 1 + 19 = 3 + 17 = 7 + 13$	3
$22 =$	
$24 =$	
$26 =$	
$28 =$	

When every prime number in the range from n to $2n$ can be paired with a prime number in the range from 1 to n so that their sum is $2n$, then $P(2n)$ has its greatest possible value. For example, when $2n = 36$ each of the prime numbers in the range from 18 to 36 (19, 23, 29, 31) can be paired with one in the range from 1 to 18 (17, 13, 7, 5) to make a sum of 36. So $P(36) = 4$, and we can call this a 'MAX'.

Q13 Is $P(30)$ also a MAX?

Q14 Investigate $P(2n)$ from $2n = 32$ to $2n = 48$.
What do you discover?
Which even numbers produce a MAX?
Check your results with the column graph in Figure 1.

Q15 What does the graph in Figure 1 tell you?

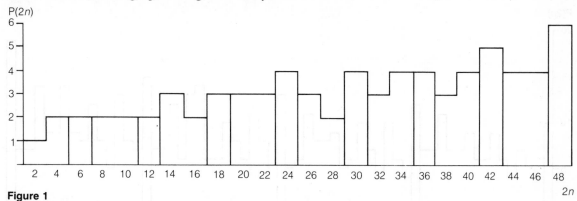

Figure 1

Q16 How many even numbers less than 50 are 1 more than a prime number?

Q17 How many prime numbers less than 100 are 1 more than a multiple of 6 (i.e. 1, 7, 13, etc.) and how many are 1 less than a multiple of 6 (i.e. 5, 11, 17, etc.)?

The column graph in Figure 2 shows P(2n) in the range 2n = 50 to 2n = 96.

Q18 What features do you notice about the graph in Figure 2?

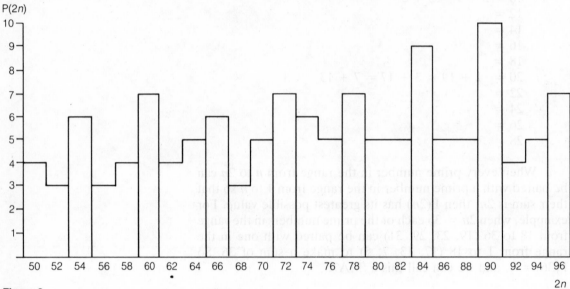

Figure 2

Some years ago, before electronic calculators became commonplace, a group of teachers taking a one-year supplementary course in mathematics at Bishop Otter College, Chichester, assisted me in making the arithmetical calculations to continue the investigation for even numbers up to 420, our only aid being a chart of prime numbers found by using the sieve pattern. The results are shown in Figure 3.

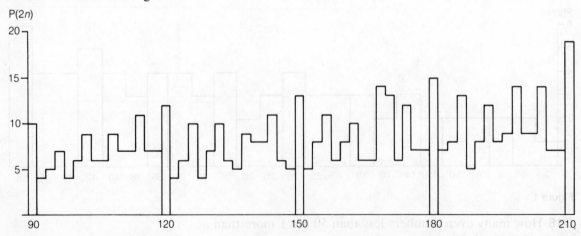

Figure 3

We were rewarded at the half-way stage by finding that P(210) was no less than 19. This was surpassed by P(270) = 20 by P(300) = 21 and by P(330) = 24. The next peak came at P(390) = 27, and we were correct in anticipating that P(420) would provide a high peak — no less than 31.

Q19 Find the prime factors of 92, 98, 122 and 128, and of multiples of 6 within this range.
Does this suggest why the latter provide higher values of P(2n) than the former?

Q20 Investigate P(90), P(120), P(150), P(180), P(210), P(240) and P(270).
Is any of them a MAX?

Q21 Why was a high peak anticipated for P(420)?
Is it a MAX?
What are the prime factors of 210 and 420?

Q22 It appears from the graph that when 2n is a multiple of $30 = 2 \times 3 \times 5$, P(2n) has a higher value than its neighbours.
Why should this be so?

Problems

1	2	3	4	5	6	7	8	9	10
11	12	13	14	15	16	17	18	19	20
21	22	23	24	25	26	27	28	29	30
31	32	33	34	35	36	37	38	39	40
41	42	43	44	45	46	47	48	49	50
51	52	53	54	55	56	57	58	59	60
61	62	63	64	65	66	67	68	69	70
71	72	73	74	75	76	77	78	79	80
81	82	83	84	85	86	87	88	89	90
91	92	93	94	95	96	97	98	99	100

The square formed by the first 100 numbers contains both 'composite numbers' that are the product of two smaller numbers (e.g. $8 = 2 \times 4$, $15 = 3 \times 5$) and 'prime numbers' that have no smaller factors (e.g. 1, 2, 3, 5, 7 etc.).

1 How many prime numbers appear in the second row?

2 Where do all the even numbers appear?

3 Where do all multiples of 5 appear?

4
```
 1   2   3   ■   5   6   7   ■   9  10
11   ■  13  14  15   ■  17  18  19   ■
21  22  23   ■  25  26  27   ■  29  30
31   ■  33  34  35   ■  37  38  39
```

What kind of numbers have been blacked out in the above diagram?
Can you describe the pattern formed by these numbers?
Is the pattern formed by multiples of 6 similar?

5   Where do all multiples of 3 appear in the square?

6   Do multiples of 9 and 11 form similar patterns?

7   Multiples of 7 also form knight's move patterns. You can now use these patterns to black out all the multiples of the prime numbers 2, 3, 5 and 7 in the number square and you will be left with only prime numbers less than 100.

8   How many of the first 100 numbers are

a   prime

b   composite?

9   The formula $n^2 + n + 5$ produces several prime numbers for values of n from 0 to 8: complete this table to find out how many primes and how many composite numbers are produced.

n	0	1	2	3	4	5	6	7	8
n^2	0	1	4						
5	5	5	5						
$n^2 + n + 5$	5	7							

10   It is thought that every even number can be expressed as the sum of two prime numbers. Investigate the number of ways in which 24, 26, 28, 30, 32, 34 and 36 can be expressed as the sum of two prime numbers.
What do you discover?

11   Choose any three prime numbers greater than 3, and find their squares and the remainders when these squares are divided by 24.
Can you explain the result?

12   If $m^2 - n^2 = p$ where m and n are integers and p is any prime number greater than 2, is it always possible to find positive numerical values for m and n?

13 Can you express each of these prime numbers — 5, 13, 17 — and their squares as the sum of the squares of two numbers?

14 $(5, 7), (11, 13), (17, 19)$ are pairs of primes that differ by 2. Find three more such pairs.

Add 1 to the product of each pair: what is the highest common factor of the resulting numbers?

15

1	3	5	7	9	11	13
15	17	19	21	23	25	27
29	31	33	35	37	39	41

If you continue this table of odd numbers only, what patterns do you find are made by multiples of the prime numbers 3, 5, 7 and 13?

Use this to find prime numbers less than 200.

(Note: $121 = 11^2$ is the only multiple of 11 left after removing multiples of 3, 5, 7, and 13.)

7 Knight's tours

The geometrical problem of moving a knight on a chessboard so that it visits each of the black and white squares once and once only was solved by the 18th century mathematicians Euler and De Moivre. Solutions using their methods are illustrated below. These are both unicursal, as the knight can move from the square numbered 64 to that numbered 1.

52	43	50	37	62	41	58	35
49	46	53	42	55	36	61	40
44	51	48	63	38	59	34	57
47	64	45	54	33	56	39	60
28	7	24	1	22	13	32	15
25	2	27	6	31	16	19	12
8	29	4	23	10	21	14	17
3	26	9	30	5	18	11	20

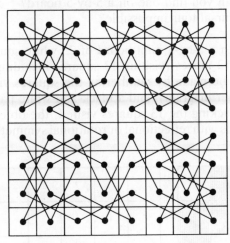

38	41	18	53	28	43	16	63
19	54	39	42	17	64	29	44
40	37	52	1	8	27	62	15
55	20	7	4	11	14	45	30
36	51	12	9	2	5	26	61
21	56	3	6	13	10	31	46
50	35	58	23	48	33	60	25
57	22	49	34	59	24	47	32

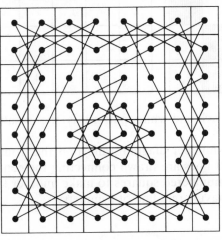

Q1 Explain why all the odd numbers appear on squares of one colour, and the even numbers on squares of the other colour.

A knight's move on a chessboard can be described as the combination of two translations, one to the right (or left) and the other up (or down). In vector notation these can be represented by giving eight possible moves.

$$\begin{pmatrix} \pm 1 \\ \pm 2 \end{pmatrix} \text{ or } \begin{pmatrix} \pm 2 \\ \pm 1 \end{pmatrix}$$

Various methods for finding knight's tours on a full-size chessboard are given in Rouse Ball's *Mathematical Recreations and Problems*. A simpler pastime is to find the patterns made by knight's tours on mini-chessboards.

Q2 No complete tours are possible on 3-by-3 or 4-by-4 miniboards, but can you find one on a 5-by-5 board?
Why is a unicursal tour impossible?

Beginning with a 5-by-5 mini-board of 25 white squares, a knight's tour of 12 moves (visiting 13 squares including the starting point) can be made by numbering the squares visited in order (the number diagram), and a black-and-white pattern can be made by blacking the 13 squares visited, the objective being to find patterns with reflectional or rotational symmetry.

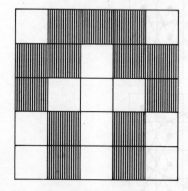 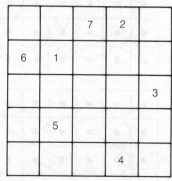 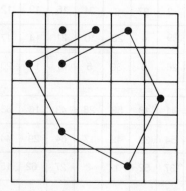

Q3 The above black-and-white pattern is the result of a knight's tour.
Complete the number diagram, and find the 'route diagram' in which lines are drawn connecting the centres of consecutively numbered squares to make another kind of pattern, also having one line of symmetry.

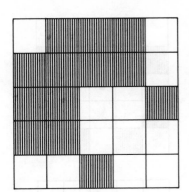 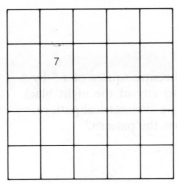 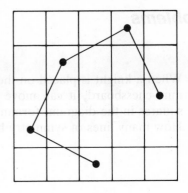

Q4 The black-and-white pattern above has symmetry about a diagonal line.
Complete the number diagram and the route diagram.
Why does 7 always appear in a square on the line of symmetry?
What is the sum of the numbers in two squares that are reflections in the line of symmetry?

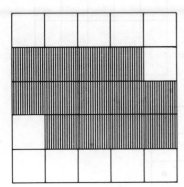 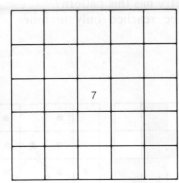 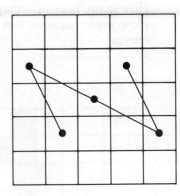

Q5 The above pattern has rotational symmetry only. Can you complete the number diagram and the route diagram?
What is the sum of the numbers in a pair of squares symmetrically placed with respect to the centre of rotation?

Q6 Invent some symmetrical knight's tours with lines or centres of symmetry to make black-and-white patterns and route diagrams. There are some which have alternative number diagrams and so have alternative route diagrams.

Problems

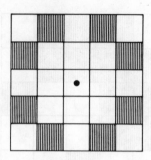

1 When a knight is placed on the centre square of a 5-by-5 mini-chessboard, it can move to any of the eight black squares in the diagram, forming a symmetrical pattern. How many lines of symmetry has the pattern?

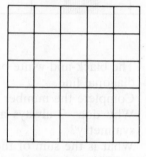

2 Copy the empty diagrams and use them to find the following.

a What pattern is made by blacking the squares to which the knight can travel in two moves from the central square apart from returning to its starting point.
How many black squares has this pattern, and how many lines of symmetry?

b What pattern is made by blacking the squares that can be reached only in three moves?
How many lines of symmetry has this pattern?
How many squares can be reached only in four moves?

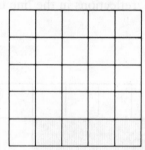

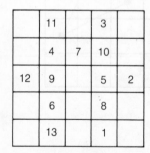
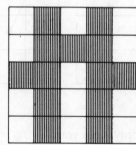
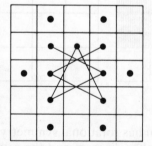

3 The numbered diagram above shows a knight's tour. By blacking the 13 squares he has occupied, the pattern with a central line of symmetry is made. By joining the centres of these 13 squares in order, a route diagram can be made by completing the next diagram.
Has it also a line of symmetry?
Can you find two other number diagrams and two other route diagrams for this black-and-white pattern?

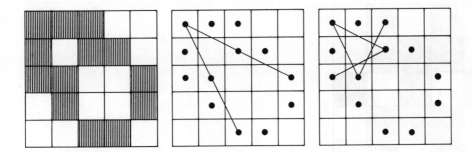

4 The black-and-white pattern above has a diagonal line of
symmetry.
Complete the two possible route diagrams.

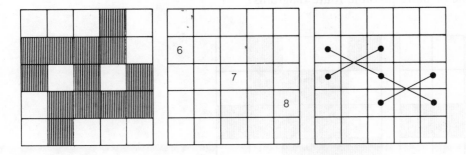

5 The black-and-white pattern above has rotational symmetry only.
Complete its number diagram and its route diagram.

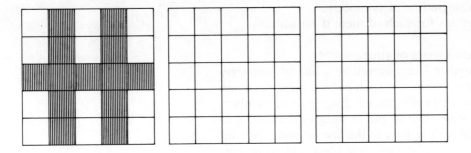

6 This black-and-white pattern has two lines of symmetry,
and consequently has rotational symmetry about the central square.
Copy the blank diagrams and use them to find route
diagrams

a with line symmetry

b with rotational symmetry.

(There are alternatives for each.)

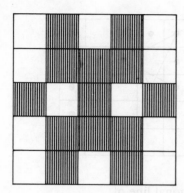

7   There is another black and white pattern with two lines
of symmetry.
Can you find one or more possible route diagrams?

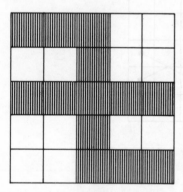   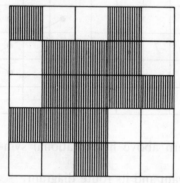

8   One of the above diagrams has rotational symmetry and
the other has a single line of symmetry.
Find route diagrams for each of them if possible.

9   Find some knight's tours of your own.
First put the number 7 in a square on a line of symmetry
or at the centre of symmetry, then put the numbers 6 and
8 in squares symmetrically placed. Each pair of numbers
whose sum is 14 can then be put in squares that are symmetrically placed with respect to the line or centre of symmetry. There are a few symmetrical black-and-white patterns that have no symmetrical route diagrams, but there
are very many with one or more symmetrical route diagrams.

8 *What comes next?*

Q1 Can you find what comes next in these number sequences?

a 7, 11, 15, 19, . . .

b 2, 3, $4\frac{1}{2}$, . . .

c 1, 2, 4, 7, . . .

Alternative answers often occur in this kind of puzzle: what comes next in the sequence 3, 5, 7, . . .? It could be regarded as a sequence of odd numbers, and so 9, 11, 13 would come next but, if this is a sequence of prime numbers, 11, 13, 17 would follow.

In the word-chain A — AT — PAT — PATE —, in which the next word is made by adding one letter to the previous word without changing the order of the letters, there are at least four words that could come next: PASTE, SPATE, PRATE, PATEN.

Q2 Can you add any six-letter words to the chain?

One method of finding what comes next in a numerical sequence is to find the differences between consecutive pairs of terms. If these differences form a sequence, the next number can be found. For example, the geometrical progression a, ar, $ar(1 - r)$, ar^2, ar^3 produces the sequence of differences $a(1 - r)$, $ar(1 - r)$, $ar^2(1 - r)$, which is another geometrical progression with the same common ratio.

Q3 What comes next in these sequences?

a 1, 3, 6, 10, . . .

b 2, 5, 10, 17, . . .

c 3, 11, 27, . . .

Q4 Can you find an algebraic formula for the *n*th term of the sequences in **Q1** and **Q3**?

Q5 What comes next when the formula is $(n^3 + 8n - 6)/3n$?

Q6   What comes next after 60, 90, 108, 120?
Which of the numbers 140, 150, 160, 165, 168, 170, 171
occur in the sequence?
Can you find a formula for the *n*th term of the sequence?

Q7   What kind of sequence of differences is produced by the
formula $An^2 + Bn + C$, where A, B, C are constants?

Q8   3/4, 5/7, 7/10, . . .
What fractions come next?
Can you find a formula for the *n*th term?
What is special about the sequence of differences between
pairs of consecutive terms?
Are the fractions increasing or decreasing?
Is it true that every fraction is greater than 2/3?

Q9

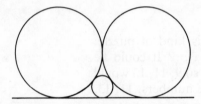

Two circles of radius 12 cm touch each other, and a third
touches them and one of their common tangents.
Can you find the radius of this circle?
Consider what comes next: a fourth circle touching the
three circles, and a fifth circle touching the fourth circle
and the original two circles, etc.
Can you find the radii of the diminishing circles in this
sequence?

Problems

1

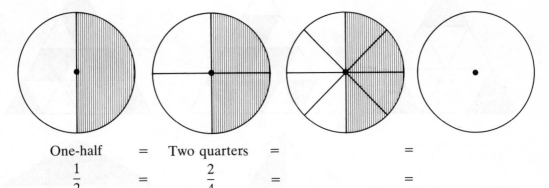

One-half   =   Two quarters   =   =

$\dfrac{1}{2}$ = $\dfrac{2}{4}$ =   =

2

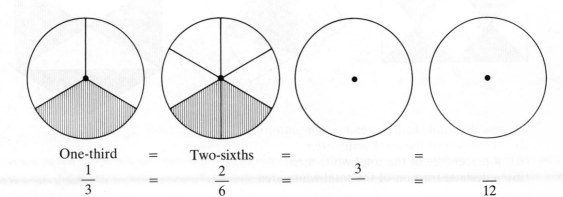

One-third   =   Two-sixths   =   =

$\dfrac{1}{3}$ = $\dfrac{2}{6}$ = $\dfrac{3}{}$ = $\dfrac{}{12}$

3   Equivalent fractions:

a $\dfrac{1}{2} = \dfrac{}{6} = \dfrac{6}{} = \dfrac{}{10} = \dfrac{11}{}$

b $\dfrac{2}{3} = \dfrac{}{6} = \dfrac{6}{} = \dfrac{}{9} = \dfrac{10}{}$

c $\dfrac{3}{4} = \dfrac{6}{} = \dfrac{}{12} = \dfrac{18}{} = \dfrac{}{36}$

4

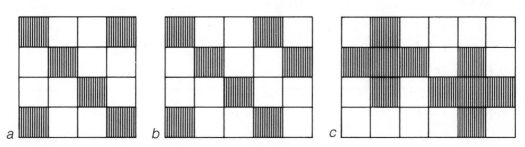

What fraction of these patterned shapes is shaded, and
what fraction is white?
Express each fraction in its lowest terms.

5

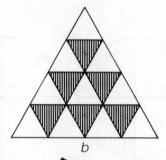 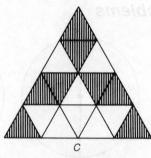

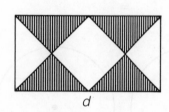 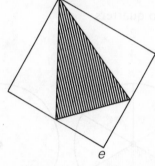 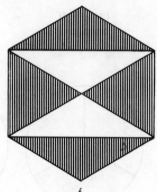

Express the total shaded area in **each** pattern as
(i)   a fraction of the total white area
(ii)   a percentage of the total white area
(iii) a decimal fraction of the total white area

6   a   Find x and y when

$$\frac{2}{5} = \frac{4}{10} = \frac{2+4}{5+x} = \frac{2+4+6}{5+x+y}$$

b   Find z, w and u when

$$\frac{3}{7} = \frac{15}{z} = \frac{3+15}{7+w} = \frac{3+15+21}{7+w+u}$$

c   If $x/y = 3/4$, which of these fractions are equivalent
     to 3/4?

   (i) $\dfrac{x + 3}{y + 4}$

   (ii) $\dfrac{2x + 3}{2y + 4}$

   (iii) $\dfrac{x + 6}{y + 8}$

   (iv) $\dfrac{3x + 9}{3y + 12}$

7 Which are the greatest and the least of these fractions?

a $\quad \dfrac{3}{4} \quad \dfrac{5}{7} \quad \dfrac{7}{10} \quad \dfrac{9}{13} \quad \dfrac{2n+1}{3n+1}$

where n is a positive integer greater than 4

b $\quad \dfrac{4}{7} \quad \dfrac{4+1}{7+1} \quad \dfrac{4+2}{7+2} \quad \dfrac{4+3}{7+3} \quad \dfrac{4-3}{7-3} \quad \dfrac{4m+1}{7m+1}$

where m is a positive integer

c $\quad \dfrac{31}{100} \quad \dfrac{33}{110} \quad \dfrac{37}{111}$

8 Continue this triangular pattern of numbers, in which each row is found by adding the pair of numbers in the row above.
You will find sequences of numbers in each of the diagonals. For example, the diagonal sloping down to the left that begins with 2, 3, 4, 5 comes from the formula $n + 1$.

```
      1 2
     1 3 2
    1 4 5 2
   1 5     2
  1         2
 1           2
```

A pseudo Pascal triangle

$$1 + 2 = 3 = 3 \times 1$$
$$1 + 3 + 2 = 6 = 3 \times$$
$$1 + 4 + 5 + 2 = \quad = 3 \times$$

a Verify that the numbers in the next parallel diagonal beginning with 2, 5, come from the formula $\frac{1}{2}n(n + 3)$

b What is the formula for the numbers in the diagonal sloping down to the right that begins with 1, 3, 5?

c What is the formula in the next parallel diagonal that begins with 1, 4?

d Verify that the numbers in the subsequent parallel diagonal that begins with 1, 5, . . . come from the formula $n(n + 1)(2n + 1)/6$, and that $1 = 1^2$, $5 = 1^2 + 2^2$, $14 = 1^2 + 2^2 + 3^2$, ...

e The table above shows the sums of the numbers in each row.
Find a formula for the sum of the numbers in the nth row of the pseudo Pascal triangle.

f You should find that one diagonal contains the sequence 2, 7, 16, 30.
The differences between consecutive terms form the sequence 5, 9, 14: what comes next in this sequence?
What comes after the 30 in the diagonal?

9 More magic square patterns

There is only one way in which the numbers from 1 to 9 can be arranged to form the Chinese magic square (Figure 1): 5 is in the central cell, and the border has the sequence 1, 6, 7, 2, 9, 4, 3, 8, clockwise or anticlockwise, with the even numbers at the corners. Note that $1 + 6 = 7$, $7 + 2 = 9$, $9 + 4 = 3 + 10$, $3 + 8 = 1 + 10$.

8	1	6
3	5	7
4	9	2

Figure 1

Q1 The diagram in Figure 2 shows the squares of the numbers in the Chinese magic square: it is not 'magic', but find the sum of the three numbers in each row, column and diagonal.
What do you discover?
Are all the sums prime numbers?

64	1	36
9	25	49
16	81	4

Figure 2

Q2 Find the pattern formed by the final digits in the square in Figure 2, and the patterns made by linking cells containing a pair of numbers

  a whose sum is 10

  b that are equal.

Q3 Investigate the square formed by the squares of the algebraic terms in the general magic square shown in Chapter 3.
What is the sum of the numbers in each row, column and diagonal?

Q4 In the Chinese magic square, find the products of the three numbers in each row, column and diagonal.
What is the sum of the products of numbers in the two diagonals?
Find also the sum of the products in the three rows, and the sum of the products in the three columns.
What do you discover?

Q5 Find the square formed by the final digits of the cubes of the numbers in the Chinese magic square, and the pattern formed by linking the cells containing pairs of numbers whose sum is 10.

Many magic squares can be made with the numbers from 1 to 16, an example of which is shown in Figure 3.

Q6 What is the sum of the four numbers in each row, column and diagonal?

Q7 What pattern is formed by linking cells in Figure 3 containing a pair of numbers whose sum is 17?

Q8 In Figure 3 what is the sum of the numbers in the four corner cells, marked P in Figure 4, and in the four central cells, marked Q?
Is it the same as the sum of the numbers in the cells marked R, and in those marked S?

Q9 Each corner of the square in Figure 3 contains four cells with one each of the letters marked P, Q, R and S in Figure 4.
What is the sum of the four numbers in each of the corners?

Q10 What pattern is formed from Figure 3 when the odd-numbered cells are black and even-numbered cells are white?
Is it symmetrical?

Q11 Do the cells containing the numbers 3, 6, 9, 12, 15 in Figure 3 form a symmetrical pattern?

Q12 Do the cells containing the numbers 5, 10, 15 in Figure 3 form a symmetrical pattern?

Q13 Two knight's moves link the cells containing the sequences $(2, 3, 4)$, $(5, 6, 7)$, $(10, 11, 12)$ and $(13, 14, 15)$ in Figure 3.
A link diagram can be formed by straight lines joining the centres of each set of cells: is it symmetrical?

Q14 Find the link diagram for the sequences $(1, 4, 3, 2)$, $(7, 6, 5, 8)$, $(10, 11, 12, 9)$, $(16, 13, 14, 15)$ in Figure 3.
Is it symmetrical?

1	12	14	7
15	6	4	9
8	13	11	2
10	3	5	16

Figure 3

P	S	S	P
R	Q	Q	R
R	Q	Q	R
P	S	S	P

Figure 4

Patterns can be used to show that in every 4-by-4 magic square there are some other sets of four cells containing numbers whose sum is the same as T, the total of the numbers in each row, column and diagonal (Figure 5).

The eight spots in the first square represent numbers in the two diagonals whose sum is $2T$. The eight spots in the second square represent numbers in the two central columns whose sum is $2T$. When added together, as in the third square, the 16 numbers have a total of $4T$. But when the numbers in the top

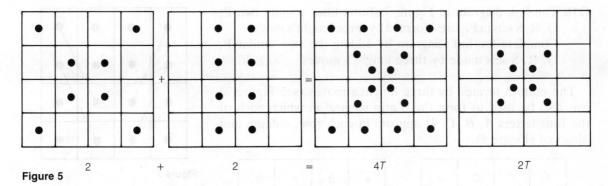

Figure 5

and bottom rows, totalling $2T$, have been subtracted, the eight remaining spots in the central block of four cells represent numbers with a sum of $2T$ (fourth square).

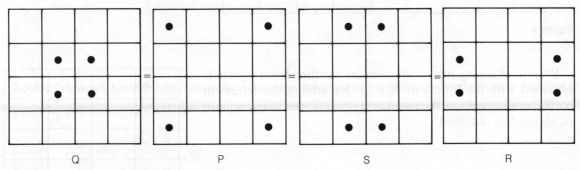

Figure 6

Figure 6 shows that the numbers in the four central cells, marked Q in Figure 4, have a sum of T. When these four cells are subtracted from the first square in Figure 5, the four corner cells, marked P, are left, and so their sum is T. Subtraction of the four central cells Q from the second square leaves the four cells marked S, whose sum is T. The four remaining cells, marked R, therefore also have a sum of T.

This result gives the reason for the answers to problem Q8.

Q15 In Figure 3 find the link patterns made by lines joining cells containing numbers that differ by

    a   8

    b   11

    c   12

    d   13

Q16 The link diagram in Figure 7 shows lines joining two P, Q, R, S sets in Figure 4 formed by three knight's moves. Complete the link diagram by adding the two similar P, Q, R, S sets made by three knight's moves.

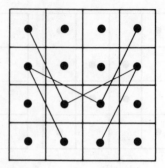

Figure 7

The pattern formed by three knight's moves (see Figure 7) can also be used to form the 'Latin square' in which each of the four letters *A*, *B*, *C*, *D* appears in each row, column and diagonal (Figure 8).

A	C	D	B
B	D	C	A
C	A	B	D
D	B	A	C

a	b	c	d
c	d	a	b
d	c	b	a
b	a	d	c

Figure 8

By interchanging rows with columns another Latin square is obtained with the letters *a*, *b*, *c*, *d*. By adding the letters in corresponding cells in the two Latin squares, the magic square in Figure 9 is obtained.

A + a	C + b	D + c	B + d
B + c	D + d	C + a	A + b
C + d	A + c	B + b	D + a
D + b	B + a	A + d	C + c

Figure 9

Q17 What is the sum of the algebraic numbers in each row, column and diagonal, and in the sets marked P, Q, R, S, in Figure 4?

Q18 Find the magic square made by putting $A = 0$, $B = 4$, $C = 8$, $D = 12$, $a = 4$, $b = 3$, $c = 2$, $d = 1$.
Find the link pattern joining cells whose numbers have a sum of 17, or differ by 8 or by 12.

Many different 4-by-4 magic squares can be made with the numbers 1 to 16 by choosing *A*, *B*, *C*, *D* from the set (0, 4, 8, 12) and *a*, *b*, *c*, *d* from the set (1, 2, 3, 4). Other 4-by-4 magic squares can be made with sets of 16 different numbers.

Q19 Investigate the magic square made by putting $A = 0$, $B = 4, C = 8, D = 13, a = 1, b = 2, c = 3, d = 4$, which has its own black-and-white patterns and difference patterns.

Paradoxically, the problem of finding 4-by-4 magic squares made with prime numbers is easier to solve than that for 3-by-3 magic squares. One has to find four sets of four prime numbers that form arithmetic progressions with the same common difference. The first sets that I found were (1, 7, 13, 19), (5, 11, 17, 23), (41, 47, 53, 59) and (61, 67, 73, 79), which have a common difference of 6. Several 4-by-4 magic squares can be made with these 16 prime numbers by choosing A, B, C, D from the set (0, 6, 12, 18) and a, b, c, d, from the set (1, 5, 41, 61).

Q20 What values for A, B, C, D, a, b, c, d produce the magic square shown in Figure 10?
What is the sum of the four numbers in each row, column and diagonal, and in the P, Q, R, S sets of four numbers?

Q21 Find the patterns formed by the remainders of the numbers in the magic square in Figure 10 after division by

5	67	13	59
53	19	61	11
79	17	47	1
7	41	23	73

Figure 10

   a   3

   b   4

   c   5

   d   6.

Are any of them magic squares?
Three of them contain only two numbers, but are their patterns all different?

Q22 The following four sets of prime numbers form arithmetic progressions with common difference 30: (13, 43, 73, 103), (23, 53, 83, 113), (41, 71, 101, 131), (67, 97, 127, 157). Make a 4-by-4 magic square with these prime numbers. Investigate the squares made by the remainders after division by 3, 4, 5 or 6.

My discovery of the knight's move patterns on the 5-by-5 square shown in Figure 11 led me to finding the pattern in which each of the five letters a, b, c, d, e appears in each row, column and diagonal of the 5-by-5 square. By interchanging rows and columns, using upper-case letters, A, B, C, D and E, and adding the numbers in corresponding cells, the algebraic pattern for

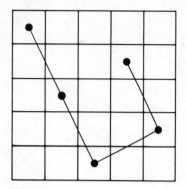
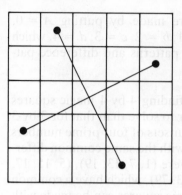

a	e	c	d	b
c	d	b	a	e
b	a	e	c	d
e	c	d	b	a
d	b	a	e	c

Figure 11

making 5-by-5 magic squares was found as shown in Figure 12(a). In order to make 5-by-5 magic squares with the numbers from 1 to 25, A, B, C, D, E can be any permutation of the numbers $(0, 5, 10, 15, 20)$ and a, b, c, d, e can be any permutation of the numbers $(1, 2, 3, 4, 5)$.

$A+a$	$C+e$	$D+c$	$E+d$	$B+b$
$E+c$	$B+d$	$A+b$	$C+a$	$D+e$
$C+b$	$D+a$	$E+e$	$B+c$	$A+d$
$B+e$	$A+c$	$C+d$	$D+b$	$E+a$
$D+d$	$E+b$	$B+a$	$A+e$	$C+c$

Figure 12(a)

Q23 What numbers must be chosen to make the 5-by-5 magic square shown in Figure 12(b)?
What is the sum of the five numbers in each row, column and diagonal, and in the four corner cells and the central cell?

21	15	8	4	17
3	19	22	11	10
12	6	5	18	24
20	23	14	7	1
9	2	16	25	13

Figure 12(b)

Q24 What pattern is formed by blacking out all multiples of 5?

As well as the 12 sets of five numbers in the rows, columns and diagonals that have a sum of 65, there are other patterned sets that have this total.
The diagrams in Figure 13 show the eight sets of 'broken diagonals' indicated by various letters. There are five more sets that

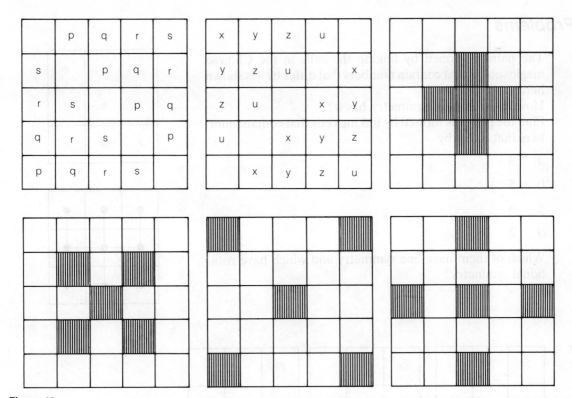

Figure 13

make the 'St. George's Cross' pattern in different positions and five more that make the domino pattern for 5 in different positions. One more is made by the extended St. George's Cross pattern and one more by the extended domino pattern. Altogether there are 32 ($= 2^5$) sets of five numbers that have the same sum in every 5-by-5 magic square made from this algebraic pattern.

In order to make 5-by-5 magic squares with prime numbers one has to find five sets of five prime numbers that form sequences whose difference are the same. The first sets that I found were (1, 7, 37, 43, 61), (11, 17, 41, 47, 71), (23, 29, 53, 59, 83), (67, 73, 97, 103, 127), (233, 239, 263, 269, 293), in which the sequence of differences is (6, 30, 36, 60).

Q25 Investigate the magic square formed by choosing A, B, C, D, E from (0, 6, 30, 36, 60) and a, b, c, d, e from (1, 11, 23, 67, 233).

What patterns are made by the remainders after division by 5, 3, or 6?

Problems

1 The pattern formed by linking the cells in the Chinese magic square that contain numbers that differ by 4 is shown here.

How many lines of symmetry has it?

Find the patterns formed by linking cells that contain numbers that differ by

a 3

b 5

c 6

d 7

Which of them have line symmetry and which have rotational symmetry?

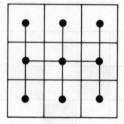

2

24	3	
9		

56		

72		

Copy these squares and complete them with numbers that are multiples of those in the Chinese magic square.

Are they magic squares?

Investigate the squares formed by the final digits of each of these squares.

What do you discover?

3 Copy this magic square and complete it by inserting numbers that make sequences in both diagonals, the middle row and the central column.

Is the sum of the numbers in the four corner cells four times the number in the central cell?

Find the patterns made by linking cells that contain numbers that differ by 1, 2, 3, 4, 5, 6, 7, 8 or 9.

Find the square formed by the remainders after division by 4.

Is it a magic square?

10	1	
	6	

4   Copy the magic square and complete it by inserting the squares of the numbers in the previous magic square. Find the sums of the three numbers in each row, column and diagonal.
What do you discover?
Investigate the square formed by the remainders after division by 4.

100	1	
	36	

5   *a*   Copy and complete the algebraic magic square with $a + b$ in the central cell and a and b in two corner cells.

   b   Find the magic square when $a = 3$ and $b = 1$.
Does it contain nine consecutive numbers?

   c   Add 1 to the number in each cell when $a = 3$ and $b = 1$.
What do you discover?

   d   Find the magic square when $a = 3$ and $b = 2$.
What numbers between 0 and 10 are missing?
What kind of pattern is made by linking cells containing numbers that differ by 1?

		$a + b$
a		b

$A + a$	$D + c$	$C + b$	$B + d$
$C + d$	$B + b$	$A + c$	$D + a$
$B + c$	$C + a$	$D + d$	$A + b$
$D + b$	$A + d$	$B + a$	$C + c$

6   The above diagram enables one to find 4-by-4 magic squares made with the numbers from 1 to 16 by choosing A, B, C, D from the set $(0, 4, 8, 12)$ and a, b, c, d from the set $(1, 2, 3, 4)$.

   a   Find the magic square when $A = 8$, $B = 0$, $C = 4$, $D = 12$, $a = 2$, $b = 1$, $c = 3$, $d = 4$.
What is the sum of the four numbers in each row, column and diagonal?

   b   Find the black-and-white pattern obtained when cells containing 3 and its multiples are black and the other cells are white.

c   What kind of pattern is made by lines linking cells containing the numbers 1, 4, 7, 10, 13, 16 that form an arithmetical progression with common difference 3?

d   What kind of pattern is made by lines linking cells containing a pair of numbers whose sum is 17?

e   Investigate the patterns made by lines linking cells containing numbers that differ by 4, 5, 6, 7, 8, 9, 10, 11, 12 or 13.

7   This diagram can be used to make 4-by-4 magic squares with the numbers from 1 to 16, or with other sets of 16 different numbers. Each row, column and diagonal has a sum $(a + b + c + d) + (A + B + C + D)$.

$A + a$	$D + c$	$C + b$	$B + d$
$C + d$	$B + b$	$A + c$	$D + a$
$B + c$	$C + a$	$D + d$	$A + b$
$D + b$	$A + d$	$B + a$	$C + c$

a   Find the magic square made by putting $A = 0, B = 4$, $C = 8, D = 12, a = 2, b = 3, c = 4, d = 1$.
What is the sum of the numbers in each row, column and diagonal?

P	S	S	P
R	Q	Q	R
R	Q	Q	R
P	S	S	P

X	X	Y	Y
X	X	Y	Y
Z	Z	W	W
Z	Z	W	W

b   What is the sum of the numbers in the four corner cells, marked P, the four central cells, marked Q, and each of the sets of four cells marked R, S, X, Y, Z, W?

c   How many lines of symmetry has the black-and-white pattern in which cells containing multiples of 5 are black and the other cells are white?

d   What kind of pattern is made by lines linking pairs of cells containing numbers whose sum is 17?

e   A wide variety of patterns can be made by lines joining cells containing pairs of numbers with the same difference, from 1 to 15, but they all have a feature in common: what is it?
Which of these 'difference patterns' has two lines of symmetry?

8 *a* What is special about the 4-by-4 magic square in which $A = 0$, $B = 30$, $C = 60$, $D = 90$, $a = 13$, $b = 23$, $c = 41$, $d = 67$?

b What black-and-white pattern is made when cells that leave a remainder of 3 after division by 10 are black and those that leave a remainder of 1 or 7 are white?

c What kind of pattern is made by lines linking cells containing the sequence of numbers ending in 3, i.e. 13, 23, 43, 53, 73, 83, 103, 113?

d Is the sum of the four numbers in each row, column, diagonal, and in the cells marked P, Q, R, S, X, Y, Z, W, a perfect square number that has only two prime factors?

e Investigate the difference patterns when the difference is a multiple of 10, from 10 to 100 inclusive. What do you discover?

f Find the squares made by the remainders after division by 3, 4, 5 or 6.
Are any of them magic squares?

g How many pairs of numbers can you find whose sum is
(i)   144?
(ii)   180?

Do the lines joining cells containing these pairs make symmetrical patterns?

9 *a* What values of A, B, C, D, a, b, c, d produce this magic square made with the numbers from 1 to 16?

b Find the patterns made by lines joining cells containing numbers
(i)   whose sum is 17
(ii)   whose sum is 9
(iii)   whose difference is 8
(iv)   whose difference is 12.

c Find the link patterns made by the consecutive numbers
(i)   from 1 to 8
(ii)   from 9 to 16.

d Investigate the difference between pairs of numbers in adjoining cells in the two left-hand columns, in the two right-hand columns, in the two top rows, and in the two bottom rows.

4	6	9	15
11	13	2	8
14	12	7	1
5	3	16	10

10 This diagram enables one to make 5-by-5 magic squares. By choosing A, B, C, D, E from the set (0, 5, 10, 15, 20) and a, b, c, d, e from the set (1, 2, 3, 4, 5), the square will contain all the numbers from 1 to 25.

$A + a$	$C + e$	$D + c$	$E + d$	$B + b$
$E + c$	$B + d$	$A + b$	$C + a$	$D + e$
$C + b$	$D + a$	$E + e$	$B + c$	$A + d$
$B + e$	$A + c$	$C + d$	$D + b$	$E + a$
$D + d$	$E + b$	$B + a$	$A + e$	$C + c$

a Find the magic square when $A = 20$, $B = 15$, $C = 10$, $D = 5$, $E = 0$, $a = 2$, $b = 3$, $c = 4$, $d = 5$, $e = 1$.
What is the sum of the numbers in each row, column and diagonal?

b Find the pattern made when odd-numbered cells are black and even-numbered cells are white.
How many lines of symmetry has this pattern?

c Find the patterns made by lines linking cells that contain
(i) pairs of odd numbers whose sum is 26
(ii) pairs of even numbers whose sum is 26
(iii) pairs of numbers that differ by 12.

d What pattern is made when cells containing numbers one more than a multiple of 3 are black and the other cells are white?

e What pattern is made when cells containing the sequence 1, 2, 3, 4, 5 are black and the other cells are white?

f On one 5-by-5 square draw lines linking the cells containing the following four sequences with a common difference of 6:
(i) 1, 7, 13, 19, 25
(ii) 2, 8, 14, 20
(iii) 6, 12, 18, 24
(iv) 4, 10, 16, 22.

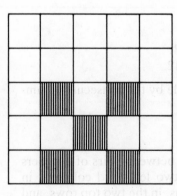

11   What is the sum of the numbers in the five cells that form the St. George's cross pattern?
There are eight other positions for this cross within the square; do they contain numbers with the same sum?

12   How many positions inside the 5-by-5 square are there for the domino pattern for 5?
Investigate the sum of the numbers in the five cells that make this pattern anywhere inside the square.

13   Can you find two similar patterns of five cells containing numbers with the same sum?

14   *a*   What is special about this magic square?
It was made by putting $A = 0$, $B = 30$, $C = 60$, $D = 90$, $E = 120$, $a = 37$.
What are the values of b, c, d, e?

37	389	241	397	167
271	307	137	97	419
197	127	449	181	277
359	151	337	227	157
367	257	67	329	211

   b   What kind of pattern is made by cells containing numbers ending with 9?

   c   Find the squares containing remainders after division by
   (i)   3
   (ii) 5
   (iii) 6.

   Are any of them magic squares?

   d   Can you make another magic square using the same values of A, B, C, D, E and using another arrangement of numbers for a, b, c, d, e?
Investigate its remainder patterns.

10 Geometrical puzzles

The ancient pastimes known as tangrams has been attributed to the Chinese: a square was cut into seven pieces that could be used to make imaginative 'pictures' (Figure 1).

The pieces can also be used in the classroom to introduce simple geometrical ideas to children and to develop their mathematical vocabulary, such as the names of shapes — square, triangle, rectangle, parallelogram — and the meaning of words — angle, size, similar, isosceles, area, fraction.

The material can be used experimentally to find what shapes can be made by fitting two or more pieces together and to solve jigsaw puzzles, e.g. to find two pieces of the same size that can be fitted together to make a square or a parallelogram, and how many pieces are the same shape but of different sizes.

A modern kind of tangram that produces a larger variety of shapes, 'pictures' and patterns was tried out at a junior school in Canterbury some years ago, when a class of nine-year-olds enjoyed a weekly period experimenting with the nine pieces of four different shapes shown in Figure 2.

A rectangular piece of cardboard measuring 2 cm by 3.5 cm is cut into rectangular quarters, two of which are then cut along a diagonal to make right-angled triangles with sides approximately in the ratio $1:\sqrt{3}:2$, and so are approximately triangles with angles of 30°, 60° and 90°, since $\sqrt{3}$ is approximately 1.75. Another quarter is cut along both of its diagonals into four triangles, two of which are approximately equilateral triangles, and the other pair are isosceles triangles.

Each child was given an envelope containing the nine pieces in two colours, and a chart was displayed showing how some 'pictures', shapes and patterns could be made with a few or all of the pieces. Each 'lesson' began with checking the contents of the envelope (one R, four Ts, two Is and two Es) and time for free experimentation and copying any discoveries in an exercise book. Meanwhile, the teacher was busy trying to guess what the pictures represented and aiding and encouraging those who were making slow progress.

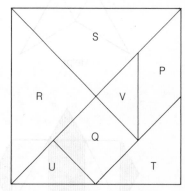

Figure 1 A traditional tangram

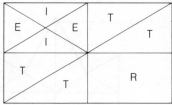

Figure 2 A modern tangram

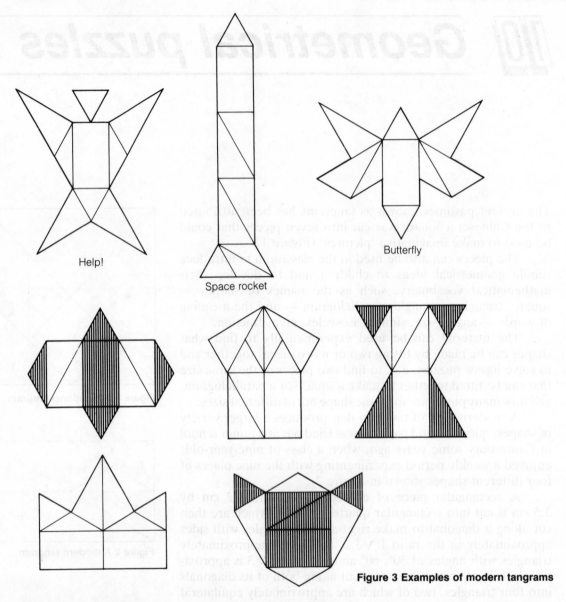

Help!

Space rocket

Butterfly

Figure 3 Examples of modern tangrams

Next simple puzzles were set, e.g. how many different shapes can be made with two T pieces (answer: 6) or can a 'diamond' shape (rhombus) be made with two I pieces, or two E pieces, or an R piece, two I pieces and two E pieces?

The most intriguing puzzles were (a) to use all nine pieces to make a large equilateral triangle, a parallelogram, or a kite, (b) to find how to fit all nine pieces together to make a symmetrical shape whose outline was shown (Figure 4), (c) to compare the areas of the pieces, and (d) to find the angles of each triangular piece as a fraction of a right angle.

An alternative and more accurate method of making the nine pieces is to dissect an equilateral triangle of any size as shown in Figure 4. It contains two small equilateral triangles, whose areas are ¹⁄₁₆ of the area of the whole triangle.

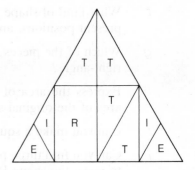

Figure 4

Q1 Can you see how to make an equilateral triangle with two or three pieces, whose area is one-quarter of the area of the whole triangle?

Q2 Can you express the areas of pieces R, TE and I as fractions of the area of the whole triangle?

Q3 Can you make an equilateral triangle whose area is ⁹⁄₁₆ of the area of the whole triangle using four pieces?

Q4 How many different parallelograms of different shapes and sizes can you make, using two pieces of the same shape?

Q5 How many different trapezia can you make, using two, three, six, eight or nine pieces?

Q6 Experiment with making symmetrical shapes — 'kites', 'arrowheads', pentagons, hexagons — using some or all of the nine pieces.

Problems

1 If you cut a square into seven pieces as shown in the diagram (a Chinese tangram), you can use them to make 'pictures' and other shapes — triangles, rectangles and parallelograms.

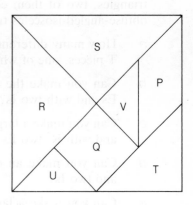

   a   Which of the pieces is a square?
         Which is a parallelogram?
         What special shape are the five triangular pieces?

   b   Which pairs of pieces are the same shape and the same size?

   c   What shape is made by R and S

         (i) in their present position

         (ii) by fitting them together in other ways?

   d   Can you use U and V to make

         (i) the shape Q

         (ii) the shape T?

   e   Can you make a rectangle with P, Q, U and V?

f What kind of shape is made by U, Q, V, P in their present positions, and by P, V, Q, T?

g Which of the pieces have two angles equal to half a right-angle?

h Express the area of each piece as a fraction of the area of the original square.

i Can you make a square with T, U and V?

j Can you find three pieces that can be fitted together to make the shape R?

k P has two obtuse angles (greater than a right-angle) and two acute angles (less than a right-angle). What is the ratio of an acute angle to an obtuse angle?

l What special shape is made by U, Q and V in their present positions? Can you make another shape with them?

2 Modern tangrams can be made as follows. Cut a cardboard rectangle, 7cm long and 4cm wide into four quarters like the rectangle R, then cut two of the quarters into four triangles, T, and finally cut the fourth quarter into four triangles, two of them equilateral triangles, E, and two obtuse-angled isosceles triangles, I.

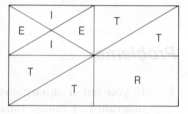

a How many different shapes can you make with two T pieces, one of which may be turned over?

b Can you make the same 'diamond' shape with two Es and with two Is?

c Can you make a larger 'diamond' shape with four Ts and with R, two Es and two Is?

d Can you make an equilateral triangle with two Es and two Is?

e Can you make a larger equilateral triangle with R, one E and two Ts?

f What kind of shape can be made by fitting together the equal sides of a T and an I?

g Can you see how to use all nine pieces to make this picture of a jumbo jet aeroplane?

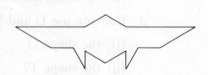

h Can you invent some pictures of your own, using all nine pieces, like those shown on the next page?

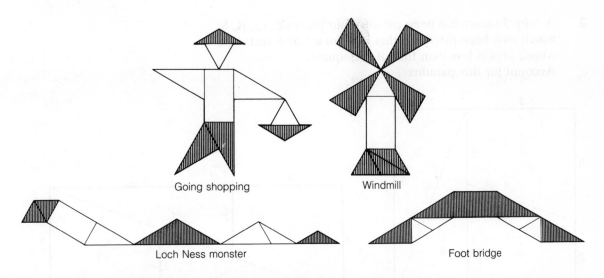

Going shopping

Windmill

Loch Ness monster

Foot bridge

i   Can you make the symmetrical shapes below, using
all nine pieces?

3   A 5-by-5 square has been cut into four pieces P, Q, R, S, which have been fitted together to form a 3-by-8 rectangle whose area is less than that of the square. Account for this paradox.

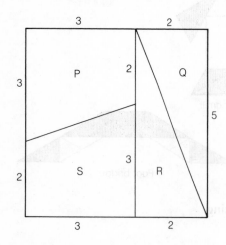

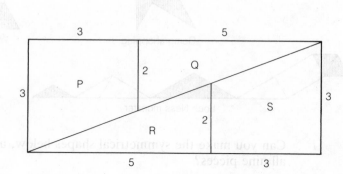

4   A 7-by-10 rectangle has been divided into four triangles. Which triangle do you think has
(i)   the least area
(ii) the greatest area?
Check your estimate by calculating the area of each triangle.

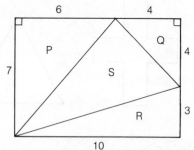

5   A 16-by-25 rectangle has been divided into two right-angled triangles, X and Z, and a quadrilateral Y.
Which piece has the greatest area?
Are X and Z similar triangles?
Calculate the lengths of the sides and the areas of X, Y and Z.
Can you fit X, Y, Z together to form a square?

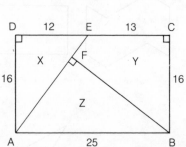

6   Which of these black-and-white patterns have the least and greatest white areas?
Do any patterns have the same black-and-white areas?

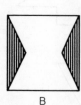

A   B   C   D   E   F

7

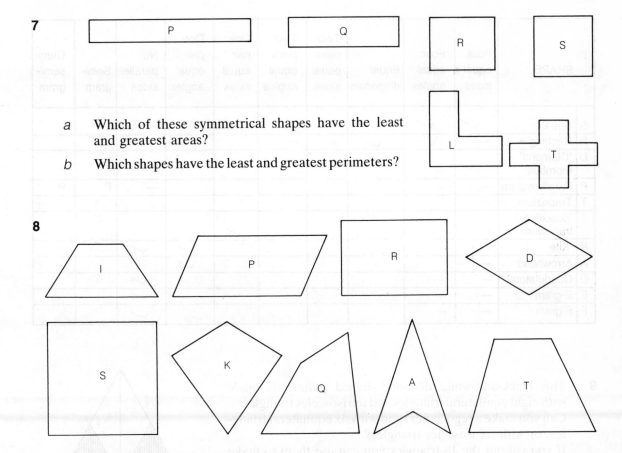

a   Which of these symmetrical shapes have the least and greatest areas?

b   Which shapes have the least and greatest perimeters?

8

Nine different kinds of quadrilateral are shown above. The E-grams below have two equal perpendicular diagonals, whereas the F-grams have two unequal perpendicular diagonals.

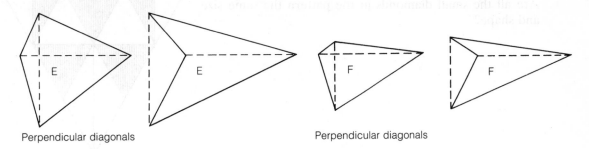

Perpendicular diagonals   Perpendicular diagonals

A 'semigram' is formed by lines joining the mid-points of consecutive pairs of sides of any quadrilateral.
Why is its area half that of the quadrilateral?
A 'demi-semigram' is the semigram of a semigram.
Draw the semigrams and demi-semigrams of the above shapes, and then complete the table on page 86.

SHAPE		Four equal sides	Four equal angles	Equal diagonals	Two pairs equal sides	Two pairs equal angles	One pair equal sides	One pair equal angles	No parallel sides	Semi-gram	Demi-semi-gram
S	Square	✓	✓	✓	—	—	—	—	—		
R	Rectangle	—	✓	✓	—	—					
D	'Diamond' rhombus	✓	—								
P	Parallelogram	—	—						—	P	P
T	Trapezium	—									
I	Isosceles trapezium	—					✓				
K	'Kite'	—						✓	✓		
A	Arrowhead	—						✓	✓		
Q	Quadrilateral	—	—						✓		
E	E-gram	—	—						✓		
F	F-gram	—	—						✓		

9 This black-and-white diamond-shaped pattern is made with eight equilateral triangles and ten isosceles triangles.
Can you make a regular hexagon with six equilateral triangles, or with six isosceles triangles?
If you cut out the 18 triangles you can use them to make your own patterns and shapes.
Can you see equilateral triangles in the pattern made with four smaller pieces, and can you make (with three isosceles triangles or four small equilateral triangles) two different sizes of equilateral triangles?
Are all the small diamonds in the pattern the same size and shape?

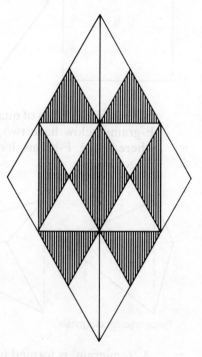

Patterns in number tables

Problems

1 Copy and continue these tables of patterned numbers for a few more rows. Some have a limited number of rows, but others never come to an end.

(*1*)
$$1 + 2 - 3 = 0$$
$$2 + 3 - 4 =$$
$$3 + 4 - 5 =$$
$$\ldots \quad \ldots \quad \ldots =$$
$$n + (n + 1) - (n + 2) =$$

(*2*)
$$1 + 2 + 3 - 4 = 2 = 2 \times 1$$
$$2 + 3 + 4 - 5 = \quad = 2 \times$$
$$3 + 4 + \qquad = \quad = 2 \times$$
$$\ldots \quad \ldots \quad \ldots \quad \ldots = \quad =$$
$$n + (n + 1) + (n + 2) - (n + 3) = \quad =$$

(*3*)
$$1 \ + \ (1 \times 1) \ = \ 1 \times 2$$
$$2 \ + \ (2 \times 2) \ = \ 2 \times$$
$$3 \ + \ (3 \times 3) \ =$$
$$\ldots \qquad \ldots \quad =$$
$$n \ + \ (n \times n) \ =$$

(*4*)
$$(1 \times 1) \ - \ (0 \times 0) \ = \ 1 + 0 \qquad = \ 1$$
$$(2 \times 2) \ - \ (1 \times 1) \ = \ 2 + 1 \qquad =$$
$$(3 \times 3) \ - \ (2 \times 2) \ = \ 3 + \qquad =$$
$$\ldots \qquad \quad \ldots \qquad = \qquad \qquad =$$
$$n^2 \ - \ (n - 1)^2 \ = \ n + (n - 1) \ =$$

(*5*)
$$(1 \times 2) \ + \ 2 \qquad = \ 2 \times 2$$
$$(2 \times 3) \ + \ 3 \qquad = \ 3 \times$$
$$(3 \times 4) \ + \ 4 \qquad =$$
$$\ldots \qquad \qquad \ldots \qquad =$$
$$n(n + 1) \ + \ (n + 1) =$$

(6) $(1 \times 1) - (2 \times 0)$ $= 1$
     $(2 \times 2) - (3 \times 1)$ $=$
     $(3 \times 3) - (4 \times 2)$ $=$
     ...   ... $=$
     $(n \times n) - (n + 1)(n - 1) =$

(7) $0 + 12 = 1 \times 12$
     $1 + 23 = 2 \times$
     $2 + 34 = 3 \times$

(8) $123 - 12 = 3 \times 37$
     $234 - 12 = 6 \times$
     $345 - 12 =$

(9) $987 - 321 = 3 \times 37 \times 6$
     $876 - 321 = 3 \times 37 \times$
     $765 - 321 = 3 \times$

(10) $012 - 1 = 11 \times$
      $123 - 2 = 11 \times$
      $234 - 3 =$

(11) $0 + 1 + 2 = 3 \times 1$
      $1 + 2 + 3 = 3 \times$
      $2 + 3 + 4 =$

(12) $1 = 1 \times 1$
         $1 + 3 = 2 \times 2$
     $1 + 3 + 5 =$

(13) $1 + \ \ 1 = 2 \times 1$
         $12 + \ 21 =$
        $123 + 321 =$

(14) $(8 \times \ \ \ 1) + 1 = 9$
        $(8 \times \ \ 12) + 2 =$
        $(8 \times 123) + 3 =$

(15) $1 - 1 = 9 \times 0$
          $11 - 2 = 9 \times$
         $111 - 3 = 9$
        $1111 - 4 =$

(16) $(9 \times 9) + 7 =$
         $(98 \times 9) + 6 =$
        $(987 \times 9) + 5 =$
       $(9876 \times 9) + \ \ =$

(17)   9 −   1 = 8
        98 −   21 =
       987 − 321 =

(18)   9 −   1 = 8
        98 −   12 =
       987 − 123 =

(19)   1 − 2 × 2 − 3 = 0
       2 − 2 × 3 − 4 =
       3 − 2 × 4 − 5 =

(20)   (7 ×   1) + 1 = 8
       (7 ×   12) + 2 =
       (7 × 123) + 3 =

(21)   9 +   1 =
        98 +   12 =
       987 + 123 =

(22)   (10 ×   0) + 1 = 1
       (10 ×   1) + 2 =
       (10 ×   12) + 3 =
       (10 × 123) +   =

(23) 1^2 $= 1$ $= 1^3$
       $(1 + 2)^2$ $= 9$ $= 1^3 + 2^3$
       $(1 + 2 + 3)^2 = 36 = 1^3 + 2^3 +$

(24)   5 +   3 = 4 × 2
         3 +   1 = 4 × 1
         1 + (−1) = 4 × 0
       (−1) + (−3) =

(25)   1 × 7 × 15873 =
       2 × 7 × 15873 =
       3 × 7 × 15873 =

(26)   3 × 7 × 5291 =
       6 × 7 × 5291 =
       9 × 7 × 5291 =

(27)   1 × 19 = (1 × 10) + 9 and 1 + 9 = 10
       2 × 19 = (3 × 10) + 8   3 + 8 = 11
       3 × 19 = (5 × 10) +   5 +   =
       4 × 19 = (× 10) +
       5 × 19 = (   ) +

$6 \times 19 =$
$7 \times 19 =$
$8 \times 19 =$
$9 \times 19 =$
$10 \times 19 =$

$1 \times 19 = (2 \times 10) - 1$ and $2 - 1 = 1$
$2 \times 19 = (4 \times 10) - 2 \qquad 4 - 2 = 2$
$3 \times 19 = (6 \times 10) - \qquad 6 - \quad =$
$4 \times 19 = (\quad \times 10) -$
$5 \times 19 = (\qquad)$
$6 \times 19 =$
$7 \times 19 =$
$8 \times 19 =$
$9 \times 19 =$
$10 \times 19 =$

(*28*) What patterns can you find in the sequences

a $\quad 2^2 - 0^2, 4^2 - 2^2, 6^2 - 4^2, \ldots, (2n)^2 - (2n - 2)^2$

b $\quad 3^2 - 1^2, 5^2 - 3^2, \ldots, (2n + 1)^2 - (2n - 1)^2$

c $\quad 3367$ multiplied by $3, 6, 9, 12, 15, 18, 21, 24, 27, 30$?

2

Sunday	Monday	Tuesday	Wednesday	Thursday	Friday	Saturday
		1	2	3	4	5
6	7	8	9	10	11	12
13	14	15	16	17	18	19
20	21	22	23	24	25	26
27	28	29	30	31		

a In the above calendar for a month of 31 days, what kind of pattern is made by blacking out
   (i) even numbers
   (ii) multiples of 3
   (iii) multiples of 4
   (iv) multiples of 5
   (v) multiples of 6
   (vi) multiples of 7
   (vii) multiples of 8?

b (i) Investigate the patterns made by the sequence 1, 7, 13, 19, 25, 31, and other arithmetic progressions with a common difference of 6.

Investigate also the patterns made by arithmetic progressions with common differences of (ii) 7, (iii) 8 and (iv) 9.

c   Find the total of the numbers in each of the three central columns, and in each of the three middle rows. What do you discover?

9	10	11
16	17	18
23	24	25

d   Any 3-by-3 square on a calendar is 'semi-magic'. What are the sums of the numbers in the central column, the middle row and the two diagonals of the example shown?

e   Can you re-arrange the nine numbers to form a magic square?

Solutions

⬛ *Number patterns*

There are only a few alternative patterns for the small numbers from 3 to 6, but there is a fascinating variety of patterns for larger numbers, of which only a few examples are shown here.

Q1 In this sequence of patterns, 1 is added at each stage to form the next pattern.

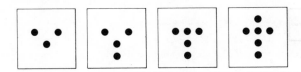

Q2

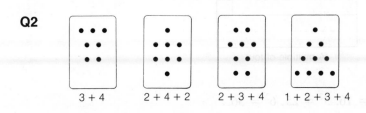

3 + 4   2 + 4 + 2   2 + 3 + 4   1 + 2 + 3 + 4

Q3 *a* One line of symmetry:

b Two lines of symmetry:

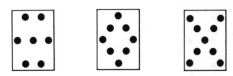

c Rotational symmetry only:

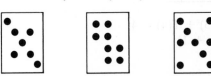

Q4 *a*   Jacks (11), A, B, F

     b   Queens (12), C

     c   Kings (13), D, E.

Q5

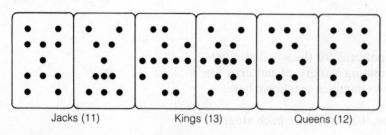

Jacks (11)   Kings (13)   Queens (12)

Q6

a

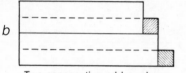

Odd + Odd = Even

b

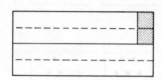

Two consecutive odd numbers   A multiple of four

Q7 *a* $1^2 = 1$, $2^2 = 4$, $3^2 = 9$, $4^2 = 16$, $5^2 = 25$, $6^2 = 36$.

        $1^2 - 0^2 = 1$, $2^2 - 1^2 = 3$, $3^2 - 2^2 = 5$, $4^2 - 3^2 = 7$
        etc.
        The differences form the sequence of odd numbers.

     b   1, 3, 6, 10, 15, 21, 28, 36, 45, 55, 66, 78, 91, 105.

        $1 + 3 = 4$, $3 + 6 = 9$, $6 + 10 = 16$, $10 + 15 = 25$.

        The sum of any two consecutive numbers is a square
        number.

     c

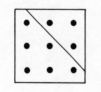 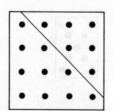

        $T(1) + T(2) = 2^2$, $T(2) + T(3) = 3^2$, $T(3) + T(4) = 4^2$
        and, generally, $T(n) + T(n + 1) = (n + 1)^2$

     d   1 3 6 10 15 21 28 36 45 55 66 78
        Two out of every three consecutive triangular numbers are multiples of 3.

Q8 *a*   Only two triangular numbers are prime numbers: 1 and 3.

 b $T(20) = \frac{1}{2} \times 20 \times 21 = 210 = 1 \times 2 \times 3 \times 5 \times 7$ which is the product of the first five prime numbers.
$T(100) = \frac{1}{2} \times 100 \times 101 = 2 \times 5^2 \times 101$.

 c $T(8) = \frac{1}{2} \times 8 \times 9 = 36 = 6^2$

$T(9) = \frac{1}{2} \times 9 \times 10 = 45$ (not a square number)

$T(16) = \frac{1}{2} \times 16 \times 17 = 8 \times 17$
 (not a square number)

$T(49) = \frac{1}{2} \times 49 \times 50 = 49 \times 25 = 35^2$

$T(99) = \frac{1}{2} \times 99 \times 100 = 50 \times 99 =$
 $2 \times 3^2 \times 5^2 \times 11$ (not a square number)

$T(144) = \frac{1}{2} \times 144 \times 145 = 2^3 \times 3^2 \times 5 \times 29$
 (not a square number)

$T(288) = \frac{1}{2} \times 288 \times 289 = (12 \times 17)^2$

The process for finding the sequence of triangular numbers that are also square numbers is beyond the scope of this book. It was published in the *Mathematical Gazette*, October 1963, Note 3067, together with some algebraic formulae such as

$$2T(n) \times T(n + 1) = T(n^2 + 2n)$$

$$T(n - r) \times T(n + r) = [T(n) - T(r)] \times [T(n) - T(r - 1)]$$

$$T(n) + T(2n) + T(2n + 1) = T(3n + 1)$$

$$T(n) + T(n + 1) + T(n^2 + 2n) = T(n^2 + 2n + 1)$$

Problems

1   The patterns represent the odd numbers 5, 7, 7, 9, 7, the central spot being the odd one. They have 4, 2, 6, 4 and 3 lines of symmetry respectively. There are several alternative patterns for the numbers from 5 to 9, for example

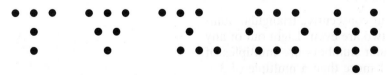

2   V-shaped patterns show the sequence of odd numbers. Hollow-square patterns show the sequence of multiples of 4.

The sequence of multiples of 3 can be shown either by rectangular patterns

or by hollow-triangular patterns

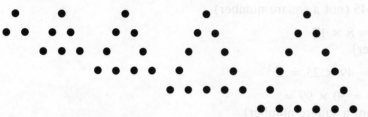

3 *a* Jacks (11), A, C

   b Queens (12), B, F

   c Kings (13), D, E, G.

There are many alternative patterns for 10, 11, 12 and 13. For example

4 *a* 1, 3, 6, 10, 15, 21, 28, 36, 45, 55, 66, 78.

   The sum of pairs of consecutive triangular numbers produces the sequence 4, 9, 16, 25, 36, . . ., i.e. the square numbers (2^2, 3^2, 4^2, 5^2 etc.).

   b If N signifies 'No' and Y signifies 'Yes', the pattern of multiples of 3 is

   N, Y, Y, N, Y, Y, N, Y, Y, . . .

   Two out of every three consecutive triangular numbers are multiples of 3.

   c True: the pattern for odd and even numbers is

   O,O, E,E, O,O, E,E . . .

   So that out of every four consecutive triangular numbers two are odd and two are even. Eight out of any 12 consecutive triangular numbers are multiples of 3, and the others are 1 more than a multiple of 3.

d   The sequence of remainders after division by 4 is

   1, 3, 2, 2, 3, 1, 0, 0,   repeated

so that there are two multiples of 4 in any set of eight consecutive triangular numbers.
The sequence of remainders after division by 5 is

   1, 3, 1, 0, 0   repeated

so that multiples of 5 occur twice in any set of five consecutive triangular numbers.
The sequence of remainders after division by 6 is

   1, 3, 0, 4, 3, 3, 4, 0, 3, 1, 0, 0   repeated

so that there are four multiples of 6 in any set of 12 consecutive triangular numbers.
The sequence of remainders after division by 7 is

   1, 3, 6, 3, 1, 0, 0   repeated

so that there are two multiples of 7 in any set of seven consecutive triangular numbers.
Similarly, it can be shown that there are two multiples of 8 in any set of 16 consecutive triangular numbers.

e $T(18) = \frac{1}{2} \times 18 \times 19 = 9 \times 19 = 171$
   $T(19) = \frac{1}{2} \times 19 \times 20 = 10 \times 19 = 190$

and these have 19 as a common factor.
Note: if n is a prime number, then $T(n-1)$ and $T(n)$ have n as a common factor.

f $T(2) - 2T(1) = 3 \ - 2 \ = 1 = 1^2$
   $T(4) - 2T(2) = 10 - 6 \ = 4 = 2^2$
   $T(6) - 2T(3) = 21 - 12 = 9 = 3^2$
   etc.

The numbers in the last column form the sequence of square numbers.

   $T(2n) - 2T(n) = \frac{1}{2} \times 2n \times (2n+1) - n(n+1)$
   $= 2n^2 + n - n^2 - n = n^2$

g $3T(2) + T(1) = 3 \times 3 + 1 = 10 = T(4)$
   $3T(3) + T(2) = 3 \times \frac{1}{2} \times 3 \times 4 + 3 = 21 = T(6)$

Similarly,

   $3T(4) + T(3) = T(8)$ and $3T(n) + T(n-1) = T(2n)$

h   True: the final digits form the pattern

   1, 3, 6, 0, 5, 1, 8, 6, 5, 5, 6, 8, 1, 5, 0, 6, 3, 1, 0,
   0   repeated

in each subsequent set of 20 triangular numbers. 2, 4, 7 and 9 never occur in this sequence. 0, 1, 5 and

6 each occur four times, and 3 and 8 each occur twice in any set of 20 consecutive triangular numbers.

i   Diamond-shaped patterns show the sequence of square numbers, 1, 4, 9, etc. whose final digits are

   1, 4, 9, 6, 5, 6, 9, 4, 1, 0 repeated

which is a palindromic pattern with the same order backwards and forwards.

No square number can have 2, 3, 7 or 8 as its final digit.

True: $(2n)^2 = 4n^2$ and $(2n + 1)^2 = 4n(n + 1) + 1$.

j $H(1) = 1$, $H(2) = 7$, $H(3) = 19$, $H(4) = 37$,
$H(5) = 61$, $H(6) = 91$.

   $H(2) = 1 + 6$
   $H(3) = 1 + 6 + 12 = 1 + 6(1 + 2) = 1 + 6T(2)$
   $H(4) = 1 + 6 + 12 + 18 = 1 + 6T(3)$

Generally,

   $H(n) = 1 + 6T(n - 1) = 1 + 3(n - 1)n$
      $= 3n^2 - 3n + 1$

   $H(1) + H(2) + H(3) = 1 + 7 + 19 = 27 = 3^3$

   $H(1) + H(2) + H(3) + H(4) = 1 + 7 + 19 + 37$
                    $= 64 = 4^3$

   $H(1) + H(2) + H(3) + H(4) + H(5)$
   $= 1 + 7 + 19 + 37 + 61 = 125 = 5^3$

Generally

   $H(1) + H(2) + H(3) + \ldots + H(n) = n^3$

Q1 The fallacy lies in the diagram. The point P, where the bisector of the angle A meets the perpendicular bisector of the base BC, always lies outside the triangle except when the triangle is isosceles, in which case the two bisectors coincide.

When AB is greater than AC, P lies outside the triangle and K lies between A and B, but N lies on AC produced. The three pairs of triangles are congruent, but AB is the sum of AK and KB, and AC is the difference between AN and CN.

Q2 *a* If $x^2 + y^2$ is an even integer, either both x and y are even or both x and y are odd. If $x = 2m, y = 2n$, then

$$\tfrac{1}{2}(x^2 + y^2) = 2(m^2 + n^2) = (m - n)^2 + (m + n)^2$$

If $x = 2m + 1$, $y = 2n + 1$, then

$$\tfrac{1}{2}(x^2 + y^2) = 2m^2 + 2n^2 + 2m + 2n + 1$$
$$= (m + n + 1)^2 + (m - n)^2$$

b $2(x^2 + y^2) = (x - y)^2 + (x + y)^2$

c $3^2 + 4^2 = 5^2$ and $5 = 1^2 + 2^2$. $5^2 + 12^2 = 13^2$ and $13 = 2^2 + 3^2$. But $9^2 + 12^2 = 15^2$ and 15 is not the sum of two squares, so we must add the proviso: 'true, when the three numbers have no common factor'. The general solution to the Pythagorean equation, $a^2 + b^2 = c^2$ in terms of integers is

$$a = k(2pq)$$
$$b = k(p^2 - q^2)$$
$$c = k(p^2 + q^2)$$

and c is the sum of two squares when $k = 1$, and a, b, c have no common factor.
It is true that if the square of any prime number is the sum of two square numbers, then the prime number itself is the sum of two square numbers.

Q3 *a* The number is

$$10000a + 1000b + 100c + 10d + e$$
$$= (a + b + c + d + e) + 9(1111a + 111b + 11c + d)$$

which is a multiple of 9 when $a + b + c + d + e$ is a multiple of 9.

b $10000a + 1000b + 100c + 10d + e$
      $= 11(909a + 91b + 9c + d) + (a + c + e) - (b + d)$

which is a multiple of 11 when $(a + c + e) - (b + d)$ is zero or a multiple of 11.

True: for example, 35 has a digit sum of 8, and $35 = 8 + 9 \times 3$. Similarly, the remainder after division by 11 can be deduced from the difference between the sums of alternate digits, or from the final number after continuous subtraction.

For example, the remainder when 324 is divided by 11 is $(3 + 4) - 2 = 5$. By continuous subtraction, 3 from 2 leaves -1, and (-1) from 4 leaves 5.

When 172 is divided by 11, the remainder is $(1 + 2) - 7 = -4$, which shows that the true remainder is $11 - 4 = 7$.

Q4   561 is a multiple of 11 since 5 from 6 leaves 1, 1 from 1 leaves 0.

    651:     6 from 5 leaves (-1). (-1) from 1 leaves 2, which is the remainder.

    1914:   1 from 9 leaves 8, 8 from 1 leaves (-7), (-7) from 4 leaves 11, which shows that 1914 is a multiple of 11.

    15851:   1 from 5 leaves 4, 4 from 8 leaves 4, 4 from 5 leaves 1, 1 from 1 leaves 0. So 15851 is a multiple of 11.

    70807:   7 from 0 leaves (-7), (-7) from 8 leaves 15, 15 from 0 leaves (-15), (-15) from 7 leaves 22, so 70807 is a multiple of 11.

    567×789: $567 = 11n + 6$ and $789 = 11m + 8$. So their product is $11k + 48$, and the remainder after division by 11 is 4.

Q5 $416614 = 4(100001) + 10(1001) + 600(11)$
        $= (4 \times 11 \times 90991) + (10 \times 11 \times 91) + (600 \times 11)$

which is a multiple of 11.

Any palindromic number with an even number of digits is a multiple of 11. For example, the number

$abcddcba = a(10000001) + 10b(100001)$
$+ 100c(1001) + 1000d(11)$

which is a multiple of 11, since any number beginning and ending with 1 and having an even number of zeros, is a multiple of 11.

Q6 The long division method for dividing 11 consists of continuous subtraction of multiples of 11, and the continuous subtraction technique is exactly equivalent. For example:

$$\begin{array}{r} 11 \overline{)\ 5638} \ \overline{\smash{\big)}\,512} \\ 55 \\ \overline{138} \\ 11 \\ \overline{28} \\ 22 \\ \overline{6} \ \ \text{remainder} \end{array}$$

5 from 6 leaves 1

1 from 3 leaves 2

2 from 8 leaves 6

which is the remainder

Q7 The man requires 11s 2d change. Two crowns (10/–) a shilling (1/–) and two pennies (2d) total 11/2d, using 5 coins.

The shopkeeper cannot accede to the customer's request for the change to be paid in different coins, but if the customer were to give him 1d, the 11/3 change could be given with 6 coins, a crown, a half-crown, a florin, a shilling, a sixpence and a threepenny bit.

Q8 £7 7s 7d = 7 × £1 1s 1d = 7 × 253d = 7 × 11 × 23d.
Mr Bookworm bought either 11 novels at 13/5 each, or 23 novels at 6/5 each: probably the former, as Mr Quackery may not have written as many as 23 novels!

Q9 The difference is always a multiple of 11d.

$$m/n - n/m = (12m + n)\text{d} - (12n + m)\text{d} = 11(m - n)\text{d}$$

Q10 The final result is always £12 18s 11d.
If the amount chosen is £x ys zd where $x > z$ then reversing the numbers, we get £z ys xd, and the difference is

$$£(x - z - 1)\ 19\text{s}\ (z + 12 - x)\text{d}$$

Reversing the digits   £$(z + 12 - x)$ 19s $(x - z - 1)$d
and adding   £12 18s 11d

Q11 The sum of the numbers in the third row above is

$$(x - z - 1) + 19 + (z + 12 - x) = 30$$

Q12 £13 − 13d = 13(240 − 1)d = (13 × 239)d

Q13 *a*

	yd	ft	in
	x	y	z
Numbers reversed	z	y	x
Difference	$x - z - 1$	2	$z + 12 - x$
Numbers reversed	$z + 12 - x$	2	$x - z - 1$
Sum	12	1	11

This is 13 in short of 13 yd which is equal to

$$13(36 - 1) \text{ in} = 13 \times 5 \times 7 \text{ in}$$

The sum of the numbers in the third row above is 13.

b   In the case of tons, hundredweight and pounds, the result is always 112 tons 18 cwt 111 lb which is 113 lb short of 113 tons.

Q14 The result is 7 gallons 7 pints, which is 1 pint short of 8 gallons = 7×9 pints, which is exactly divisible by 7 and 9.

Q15 The result is 999 litres 999 cm^3, which is 1 cm^3 short of 1000 litres which is equal to

$$999 \times 1001 \text{ cm}^3 = 3^3 \times 7 \times 11 \times 13 \times 37 \text{ cm}^3$$

Problems

1   The copper coins are worth $3d + 7\frac{1}{2}d + 23d = 33\frac{1}{2}d = 2/9\frac{1}{2}$. The silver coins are worth $2/3 + 2/6 = 4/9$. So Alice has saved $7/6\frac{1}{2}$, and so must save $3/5\frac{1}{2}$ more to pay 11/– for the books.

2 $1000d = £4/3/4$, but 100/–, 50 florins and 40 half-crowns are each worth £5, which is the largest sum of money.

3   Stamps for 32 letters and 17 postcards cost $40\frac{1}{2}d = 3/4\frac{1}{2}$, and the change from 5/– would be $1/7\frac{1}{2}$.

4   Alice is 5 years older than Caroline, and Beatrice is 3 years older than Caroline. So we subtract $(5 + 3)$ years from the total of 23 years = 15 years, and one-third of this is Caroline's age = 5 years. Alice is 10 years old and Beatrice is 8 years old.
The sum of their ages in 23 years' time will be $4 \times 23 = 92$ years.

5 $5\frac{3}{4}$ periods of 4 years = 23 years, which was the real age of the Mad Hatter when he met Alice, and the March Hare was 22 years old.

6 *a* YARD — CARD — CARE — MARE — MIRE — MILE.

  b ACE — ARE — ORE — ONE.

  c ZERO — HERO — HERD — HARD — HARE — HALE — HALF.

  d COST — MOST — MAST — MALT — SALT — SALE.

  e SLOW — SLOT — CLOT — COOT — COST — CAST — FAST.

  There may be other shorter solutions.

7 *a* $(21 - x) + x + (18 - x) = 26$. So $x = 13$.

  b $(20 - y) + y + (13 - y) = 26$. So $y = 7$.

8 All are multiples of 9 except the last, 10201, which has a digit sum of 4, and so leaves a remainder of 4 after division by 11. Both 123 and 321 are multiples of 3 (since their digit sums are multiples of 3) and so their product is a multiple of 9.
We need not find the digit sum in 123456789, as $1 + 8 = 2 + 7 = 3 + 6 = 4 + 5 = 9$, and so the digit sum must be a multiple of 9.

9 48 and 84 are both multiples of 3, and so their product is a multiple of 9. But 4132 has a digit sum of 10, and so it is not a multiple of 9.

10 No. Each number leaves a remainder of 3 after division by 9, and so their sum leaves a remainder of 6 after division by 9.

11 The sums of alternate digits of 123321 and 365,365 are the same, and the difference between the sums of alternate digits of 50105 is 11, so all three numbers are multiples of 11.
$10^2 + 1 = 101$, and $10^4 + 1 = 10001$, and both leave remainder of 2 after division by 11, but $10^3 + 1$ (and $10^n + 1$, when n is any odd number) is a multiple of 11.
Note: any six-digit patterned number, *abc,abc*, is a multiple of 11. Obviously *abc* is also a factor: can you find the other prime factors?

12   If the four digits are a, b, c, d, then

$$(1000a + 100b + 10c + d) - (1000d + 100c + 10b + a)$$
$$= 999a + 90b - 90c - 999d$$

which is a multiple of 9. The sum of the two numbers is

$$1001(a + d) + 110(b + c)$$
$$= 11 \times 91(a + d) + 11 \times 10(b + c)$$

which is a multiple of 11.

13   The final number is always the same as the chosen number. If n is the number chosen in the range 2 to 11 inclusive, then $(n - 2)$ is in the range 0 to 9 inclusive.

Add 9 to n: $n + 9$
Multiply $(n + 9)$ by 2: $2n + 18$
Subtract n from $(2n + 18)$: $n + 18$

But $(n + 18) = 20 + (n - 2)$, and since $(n - 2)$ is in the range 0 to 9, it is the units digit in the final number, and the tens digit is 2.
The sum of these digits is $2 + (n - 2) = n$.

14 $5U + T$ is always a multiple of 7. When divided by 7 the quotients form the sequence 5, 3, 1, 6, 4, 2, 0, repeated.

15   If $10a + b$ is a multiple of 7, where a can be more than 10 and b is less than 10, then $10a + b = 7m$ shows that $50a + 5b = 5 \times 7m$, and so $a + 5b = 7(5m - 7a)$. In words, five times the units digit added to the number formed by the remaining digits is a multiple of seven only when the original number is a multiple of seven.

16   All except the last number, 12321, are multiples of 7.

17   *a*   The patterned number *abba* is a multiple of 11, as the sums of alternate digits are both $(a + b)$. The number is

$$1000a + 100b + 10b + a = 1001a + 110b$$

which is a multiple of 7 for all values of a, but b must be either 7 or 0.

   b   The patterned number *ababa* is $10101a + 110b$. But 10101 is a multiple of 7, so that a can be any number, but b must be either 7 or 0.

   c   The patterned number *abbba* $= 10001a + 1110b$ $= 5a + 4b + 7(1428a + 158b)$, which is a multiple of 7 when $5a + 4b = 7m$. This is satisfied by $a = 1$, $b = 4$, which produces the smallest number 14441.

d The patterned number

$$aba = 100a + 10b + a = 7(14a + b) + 3(a + b)$$

which is a multiple of 7 when $a + b = 7$ or 14.

18 If the number $10T + U$ is a multiple of $8 = 8m$, then $2T + U = 8(m - T)$ which is a smaller multiple of 8. 192, 216 and 704 are multiples of 8, the others are not. Since 1000 is a multiple of 8, any number of thousands will be a multiple of 8, and so the figures above 1000 can be ignored and only the last three digits need to be tested. To test 752, $T = 75$ and $U = 2$, so $2T + U = 152$. Now $T = 15$ and $U = 2$, so $2T + U = 32$, which is a multiple of 8. It follows that 752 and 752752 are multiples of 8, as are 1936 and 1020408 also.

19 If $10T + U = 12m$, then $2T - U = 12(T - m)$. This test on 312 produces $62 - 2 = 60$, a multiple of 12.

3108 produces $620 - 8 = 612$, and 612 produces $122 - 2 = 120$, a multiple of 12.

6804 produces $1360 - 4 = 1356$, 1356 produces $270 - 6 = 264$, and 264 produces $52 - 4 = 48$ (and 48 produces $8 - 8 = 0$).

20 If $10T + U = 13m$, then $40T + 4U = 13(4m)$, and so $T + 4U = 13(4m - 3T)$. All the numbers are multiples of 13.

21 $10T + U$ is a multiple of

a 17 when $T + 12U$ or $T - 5U$ is a multiple of 17

b 19 when $T + 2U$ is a multiple of 19

c 23 when $T + 7U$ is a multiple of 23

d 29 when $T + 3U$ is a multiple of 29

e 31 when $T - 3U$ is 0 or a multiple of 31

f 89 when $T + 9U$ is a multiple of 89.

3 Magic squares

Q1

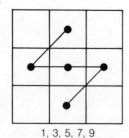

1, 3, 5, 7, 9

Q2 3, 5, 7: difference 2
1, 5, 9: difference 4
4, 5, 6: difference 1
2, 5, 8: difference 3

Q3

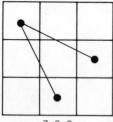 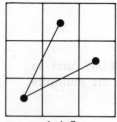 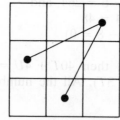 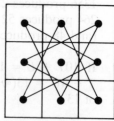

7, 8, 9   1, 4, 7   3, 6, 9   All four sequences

9	1	8
5	6	7
4	11	3

Q4 $x = 5$, $y = 7$.

Q5 Diagonal sequences 4, 6, 8 and 3, 6, 9.
Middle row 5, 6, 7.
Central column 1, 6, 11.

Q6

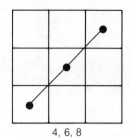

4, 6, 8   1, 3, 5, 7, 9, 11

Q7 The number in the central cell is always the average of the nine numbers in the magic square.

Q8 If $a = 2b$ the magic square is as given below. Two cells contain $m - b$, and two cells contain $m + b$.

$m + 2b$	$m - 3b$	$m + b$
$m - b$	m	$m + b$
$m - b$	$m + 3b$	$m - 2b$

Q9

15	1	11
5	9	13
7	17	3

The magic square contains the first nine odd numbers, from 1 to 17, and the multiples of 3 lie on a diagonal.

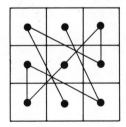 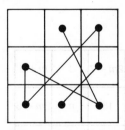

The sequence of odd numbers makes a pattern with rotational symmetry, but the sequence of prime numbers (omitting 9 and 15), does not make a pattern.

Q10

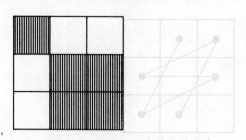

43	1	67
61	37	13
7	73	31

All the numbers in the magic square are prime numbers.
Cells containing the numeral 3 form a symmetrical pattern with one line of symmetry.
Also, those containing the numeral 1 from a V-shaped pattern, and those containing the numeral 7 lie on a diagonal.

Q11 Yes: cells linked by the V-shaped pattern (two knight's moves) always form a sequence.

Central column: $m - a - b$, m, $m + a + b$;
  difference $a + b$.
Middle row: $m - a + b$, m, $m + a - b$;
  difference $a - b$.
First diagonal: $m + a$, m, $m - a$;
  difference $- a$.
Second diagonal: $m + b$, m, $m - b$;
  difference $- b$.

Q12 Yes: the pattern formed by the sequence of the numbers from 1 to 9 has rotational symmetry.

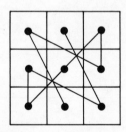

Q13

9	1	14
13	8	3
2	15	7

$m = 8$

19	1	19
13	13	13
7	25	7

$m = 13$

$2m - 7$	1	$m + 6$
13	m	$2m-13$
$m - 6$	$2m - 1$	7

This last diagram shows that whatever number m is placed in the central cell, the adjoining cell contains the number 13.

Problems

1

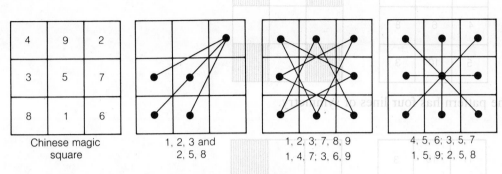

4	9	2
3	5	7
8	1	6

Chinese magic
square

1, 2, 3 and
2, 5, 8

1, 2, 3; 7, 8, 9
1, 4, 7; 3, 6, 9

4, 5, 6; 3, 5, 7
1, 5, 9; 2, 5, 8

The lines linking 1, 2, 3 form an arrow-head pattern about
the line linking 2, 5, 8 as a line of symmetry.
Both of the other patterns have four lines of symmetry.

2

8	18	4
6	10	14
16	2	12

7	17	3
5	9	13
15	1	11

The first magic square contains the first nine even numbers,
and the second contains the first nine odd numbers.

8	8	4
6	0	4
6	2	2

7	7	3
5	9	3
5	1	1

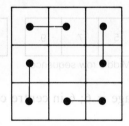

The squares filled with the final figures of both of these
magic squares have pairs of repeated figures in adjoining
cells. The sums of the numbers in the rows, columns and
diagonals of the first are either 10 or 20 and, in the second,
either 7 or 17.
The pattern formed by lines linking cells with the same
number has rotational symmetry.

3 No. One diagonal contains three 2s.
The black-and-white pattern has both diagonals as lines
of symmetry.

4

9	2	7
4	6	8
5	10	3

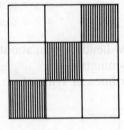

The pattern has four lines of symmetry.

5

11	13	3
1	9	11
15	5	7

The pattern has two lines of symmetry.

6

11	4	9
6	8	10
7	12	5

13	1	10
5	8	11
6	15	3

6	7	11
13	8	3
5	9	10

7

8	3	10

Top row

5	7	9

Middle row sequence

4	11	6

Bottom row

8   3 + 8 + 7 = 18; average = 6; 6 in centre cell.

3	8	7

5	4	9
10	6	2
3	8	7

The Chinese magic square with 1 added to each cell.
Sequence differences 1, 2, 3, 4.

9 *a*

2	1	3
3	2	1
1	3	2

b

11	4	9
6	8	10
7	12	5

c

13	5	12
9	10	11
8	15	7

d

3	2	7
8	4	0
1	6	5

e

7	3	8
7	6	5
4	9	5

f

8a	3a	7a
5a	6a	7a
5a	9a	4a

b and *d* contain nine consecutive numbers.

10 *a*   The Chinese magic square.

b   The magic square containing the first nine odd numbers.

c   A prime number square:

101	5	61
29	59	89
47	113	17

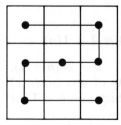

$m = 11$, $x = 4$, $y = 6$.

4 *Pythagoras and his theorem*

Q1 The triangles ABC, ACN, CBN are similar, since each has one right-angle and the pair of complementary angles A and B. Hence $a/x = c/a$, and $b/(c - x) = c/b$, i.e. $a^2 = cx$, $b^2 = c^2 - cx$, and by addition $a^2 + b^2 = c^2$.

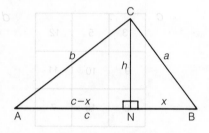

Q2 The similar triangles ABC, ACN, CBN have hypotenuses in the ratio $c:b:a$, and so their areas are proportional to c^2, b^2 and a^2, i.e. their areas are kc^2, kb^2, ka^2. But the area of $\triangle$ABC = area of $\triangle$ACN + area of $\triangle$CBN, and so

$$kc^2 = kb^2 + ka^2, \text{ i.e. } a^2 + b^2 = c^2$$

Q3 The right-angled triangle ABC, with sides a, b, c, appears three more times in the diagram above as $\triangle$BNM, $\triangle$PKN and $\triangle$AHP, to form the pentagonal shape ACMNP, with sides b, $a + b$, a, c, c.

When the last two triangles are removed from the pentagon, the squares a^2 and b^2 remain, but if the first two triangles are removed, the square c^2 remains. Hence $a^2 + b^2 = c^2$.

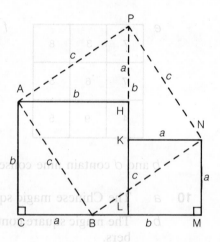

Q4 When $a = 2n + 1$,

$$a^2 = 4n^2 + 4n + 1 = (2n^2 + 2n) + (2n^2 + 2n + 1)$$

which is the sum of two consecutive numbers.

Take $b = 2n^2 + 2n$, $c = 2n^2 + 2n + 1$, then

$$c^2 - b^2 = (c - b)(c + b) = 1 \times (4n^2 + 4n + 1)$$
$$= (2n + 1)^2 = a^2$$

and so $a^2 + b^2 = c^2$.

Note: $b = 2n(n + 1) = 4 \times \tfrac{1}{2}n(n + 1) = 4 \times T(n)$.

Q5 The Pythagorean formula $a = 2n + 1$, $b = 2n(n + 1)$, $c = 2n(n + 1) + 1$ produces an infinity of sets (a, b, c) for sides of right-angled triangles in which $c - b = 1$, or $c = b + 1$.

Hence when $c = 1^2 + 12^2 = 145$, b must be $144 = 12^2$, $144 = 4 \times 36$, and 36 is the 8th triangular number.

$$a^2 = c^2 - b^2 = (c - b)(c + b) = 1 \times (145 + 144)$$
$$= 289 = 17^2$$

Hence $a = 17$, $b = 144$, when $c = 145$.

Q6 If $(2x + 1)^2 + (3x + 1)^2 = (4x + 1)^2$, then $4x^2 + 4x + 1$ $= (4x + 1)^2 - (3x + 1)^2 = x(7x + 2) = 7x^2 + 2x$.
Hence $3x^2 - 2x - 1 = 0 = (3x + 1)(x - 1)$, and $x = 1$ or $-1/3$.
When $x = 1$ we obtain the right-angled triangle $(3, 4, 5)$ and when $x = -1/3$, $a = +1/3$, $b = 0$, $c = -1/3$.

Q7

	$a = 2m$	$b = m^2 - 1$	$c = m^2 + 1$
$m = 2$	4	3	5
$m = 3$	6	8	10
$m = 4$	8	15	17
$m = 5$	10	24	26

All except $m = 4$ produce multiples of the $(3, 4, 5)$ and $(5, 12, 13)$ sets produced by the Pythagorean method.

Q8 When $m = 2n + 1$, $a = 2(2n + 1)$, $b = 4n(n + 1)$, $c = 2(2n^2 + 2n + 1)$, so that (a, b, c) are double the set $a = 2m + 1$, $b = 2m(m + 1)$, $c = 2m^2 + 2m + 1$, which is produced by the Pythagorean method.

Q9 When $m = 5$ and $n = 2$, $a = 20$, $b = 21$, $c = 29$, and $a = b - 1$.

Q10 Assume that a pair of numbers, m and n, with no common factor, can be found to satisfy $m^2 = 2n^2$, i.e. $m/n = \sqrt{2}$. Then m must be even since its square $(2n^2)$ is even. Write $m = 2k$, then $m^2 = 2n^2 = 4k^2$. Hence $n^2 = 2k^2$, which shows that n must also be even. This contradicts the assumption that m and n have no common factor and so that assumption was false: the square root of 2 cannot be a rational fraction m/n, where m and n have no common factor.
Note: every fraction km/kn can be expressed as an irreducible equivalent fraction m/n, where m and n have no common factor, by dividing numerator and denominator by k.

Q11 The sides of an isosceles right-angled triangle are in the ratio $1:1:\sqrt{2}$. The right-angled triangle with sides $(20, 21, 29)$ is approximately isosceles, and so the ratio of its sides is approximately $1:1:\sqrt{2}$, i.e. $29/20$ and $29/21$ are each approximately $\sqrt{2}$. $29/20 = 1.45$ and $29/21 = 1.238 \ldots$ and $\sqrt{2} = 1.414 \ldots$ ..

Problems

1   The four pieces of the 4-by-4 square form a border to the 3-by-3 square.

2   Only four pieces are needed: one a 3-by-3 square, and three rectangles, 1 by 2, 2 by 3 and 2 by 4 which form the 4 by 4 square.

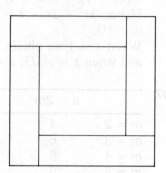

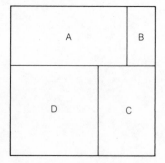

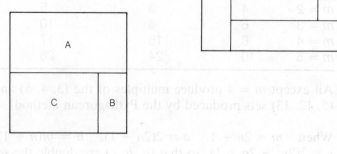

3   There are 9, 16 and 25 small triangles.
Two dissections are possible.

(1)   Cut off a triangle with 16 small triangles, and divide the remaining strip into three pieces containing 1, 3 and 5 small triangles to form the smallest of the original three equilateral triangles.

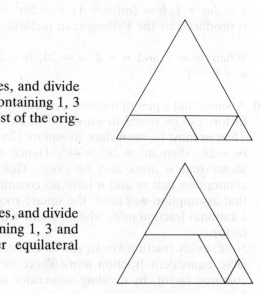

(2)   Cut off a triangle with nine small triangles, and divide the remainder into three pieces containing 1, 3 and 12 small triangles to form the other equilateral triangle.

4   The diagram shows how to fit together the five rectangular pieces to form a 12-by-12 square, showing that $5^2 + 12^2 = 13^2$.

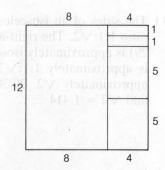

5 Each of the smaller rectangles must be cut into three equal pieces, which fit on to the largest rectangle to form a 24-by-24 square, showing that $7^2 + 24^2 = 25^2$.

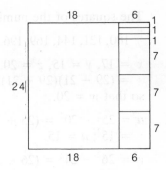

6

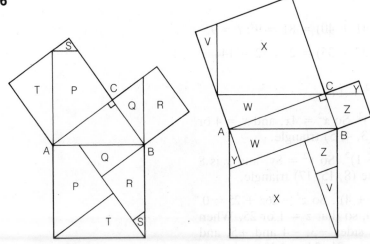

T is identical with $\triangle ABC$, and Q and S are similar to it. R and S can be fitted together to make T, and so T can be interchanged with R and S.

7 The piece W is identical with the $\triangle ABC$, and V and Y are similar to it. Z and V can be fitted together to make $\triangle ABC$ or the piece W, and so can be interchanged with it.

8 *a* Since C is a right angle, $A + B = C$, and each of the three triangles contains the angles A, B, C and so are similar to each other. Their hypotenuses are a, b and c respectively, and so the ratio of corresponding sides is $a:b:c$.

b The heights of similar triangles are proportional to their bases, and so their areas are proportional to the squares on corresponding sides, i.e. to $a^2:b^2:c^2$.

c Hence the areas of the three triangles are ka^2, kb^2 and kc^2, where k is a suitable constant. But the sum of the two smaller triangles equals the area of the original $\triangle ABC$, so that $ka^2 + kb^2 = kc^2$, showing that $a^2 + b^2 = c^2$.

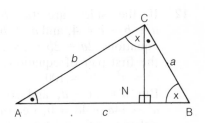

9   The squares of the numbers from 10 to 21 are

   100, 121, 144, 169, 196, 225, 256, 289, 324, 361, 400, 441

$x = 17$, $y = 15$, $z = 20$, $w^2 = 29^2 - 21^2$
   $= (29 - 21)(29 + 21) = 8 \times 50 = 400 = 20^2$
so that $w = 20$.

$u^2 = 25^2 - 20^2 = (25 + 20)(25 - 20) = 45 \times 5 = 225$
   $= 15^2$; $u = 15$.

$v^2 = 26^2 - 24^2 = (26 - 24)(26 + 24) = 2 \times 50 = 100$;
$v = 10$.

$t^2 = 41^2 - 40^2 = (41 - 40)(41 + 40) = 81 = 9^2$; $t = 9$.

$s^2 = 37^2 - 35^2 = (37 - 35)(37 + 35) = 2 \times 72 = 144$
   $= 12^2$; $s = 12$.

$365 = 10^2 + 11^2 + 12^2 = 13^2 + 14^2$

10   a $x^2 + (x - 1)^2 = (x + 1)^2$. So $x^2 = 4x$, and $x = 4$ or
       0. $x = 4$ produces the $(3, 4, 5)$ triangle.

   b $y^2 + (2y - 1)^2 = (2y + 1)^2$. So $y^2 = 8y$, and y is 8
       or 0. $y = 8$ produces the $(8, 15, 17)$ triangle.

   c $(z - 4)^2 + (z - 5)^2 = (z + 4)^2$. So $z^2 - 26z + 25 = 0$,
       i.e. $(z - 1)(z - 25) = 0$, so that $z = 1$ or 25. When
       $z = 1$, the triangle has sides -3, -4 and $+5$, and
       when $z = 25$, the sides are 21, 20 and 29.

11   If $3x - 2$ is the hypotenuse, then $x^2 + (2x + 2)^2 =$
   $(3x - 2)^2$, and so $4x^2 = 20x$, and $x = 5$ or 0.
   $x = 5$ produces the triangle $(5, 12, 13)$.
   If, however, $2x + 2$ is the hypotenuse, then
   $x^2 + (3x - 2)^2 = (2x + 2)^2$, and so $6x^2 = 20x$, and
   $x = 10/3$ or 0.
   $x = 10/3$ produces the triangle $(10/3, 24/3, 26/3)$, which is
   similar to the $(5, 12, 13)$ triangle, but two-thirds of its size.

12   If the sides are (a, b, c), then $a + b + c = 24$,
   $a + b - c = 4$, and $a^2 + b^2 = c^2$. Adding the first pair of
   equations, $2a + 2b = 28$, and so $a + b = 14$. Subtracting
   the first pair of equations, $2c = 20$, and so $c = 10$, and
   $c^2 = a^2 + b^2 = 100$.
   But $b = 14 - a$, and so $a^2 + (14 - a)^2 = 100$. Hence
   $a^2 - 14a + 48 = 0$, i.e. $(a - 6)(a - 8) = 0$, so that a is
   either 6 or 8, and b is either 8 or 6.
   The sides of the triangle are 6 cm, 8 cm and 10 cm: its
   area is $\frac{1}{2}(6 \times 8)$ cm$^2 = 24$ cm^2, which is less than the area
   of a square of side 5 cm.

Jigsaw puzzles

Q1 The four pieces can make two rectangular shapes, a rhombus, four different parallelograms with rotational symmetry, and the quadrilateral (kite or rhombus) and pentagon shown below.

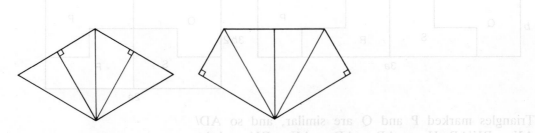

Q2 The rectangle A can be dissected in one way only, into two 'dominoes', and the T-shape B can only be cut into two unequal pieces. The other shapes, C, D, E, F, can all be dissected in two different ways.

Q3

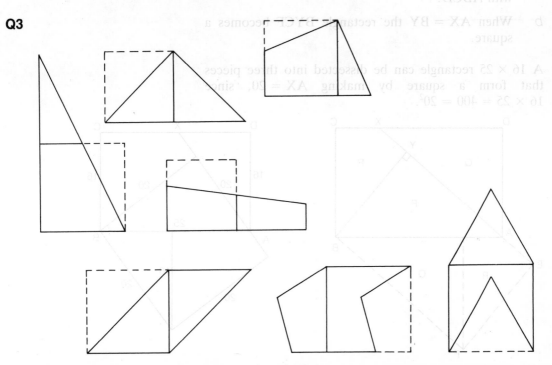

Q4

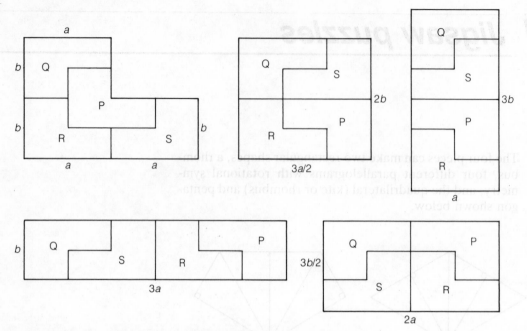

Q5   Triangles marked P and Q are similar, and so AD/
AX = BY/AB. Hence AB × AD = AX × BY, and the
rectangle with sides AX and BY has the same area as the
rectangle ABCD.

a   When AX = AB, the rectangle BYEF is identical
with ABCD.

b   When AX = BY the rectangle BYCF becomes a
square.

A 16 × 25 rectangle can be dissected into three pieces
that form a square by making AX = 20, since
16 × 25 = 400 = 20².

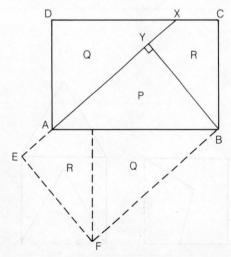

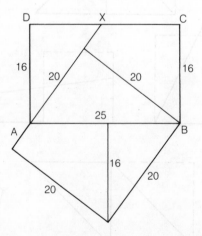

This method can be used for dissecting other rectangles, except those that are long and thin, in which case the method shown in **Q6** is preferable.

Q6

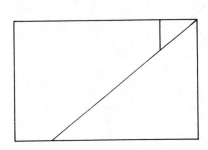 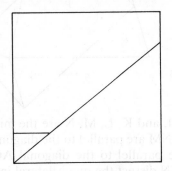

Q7

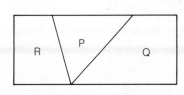

M and N are mid-points of the sides AC and BC, and KL is any line perpendicular to MN and AB.

Q8

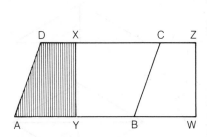 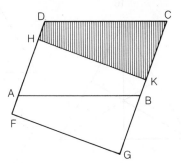

Any line perpendicular to a pair of opposite sides of a parallelogram will divide it into two pieces that can form a rectangle.

Q9

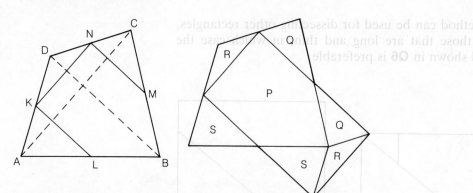

ABCD is any quadrilateral, and K, L, M, N are the mid-points of its sides. KL and NM are parallel to the diagonal DB, and KN and LM are parallel to the diagonal AC. Cuts along KL, NM and KN dissect the quadrilateral into four pieces P, Q, R and S: they form a parallelogram as shown in the second diagram.

Q10 The six pieces of the dissected regular pentagon form a square as shown in the diagram.

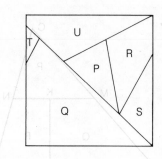

Problems

1

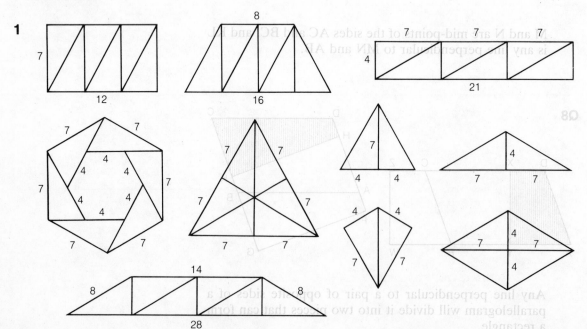

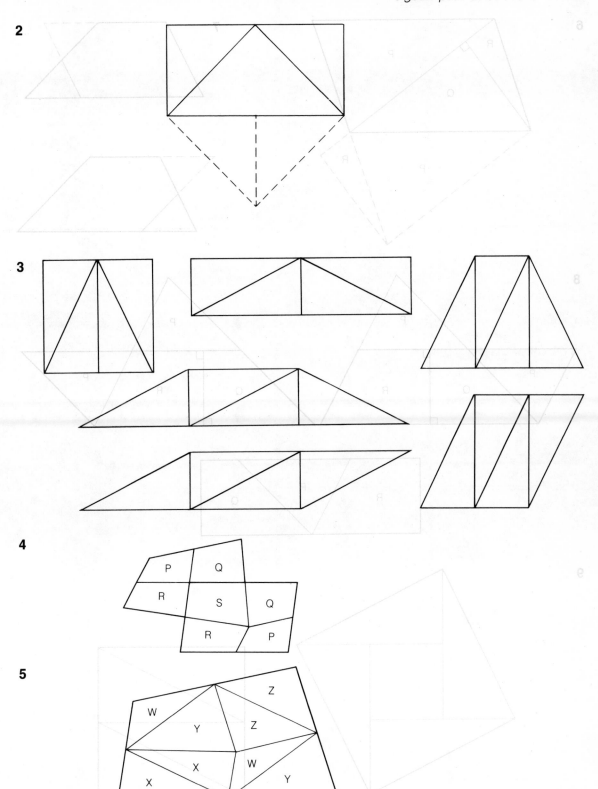

2

3

4

5

6

7

8

9

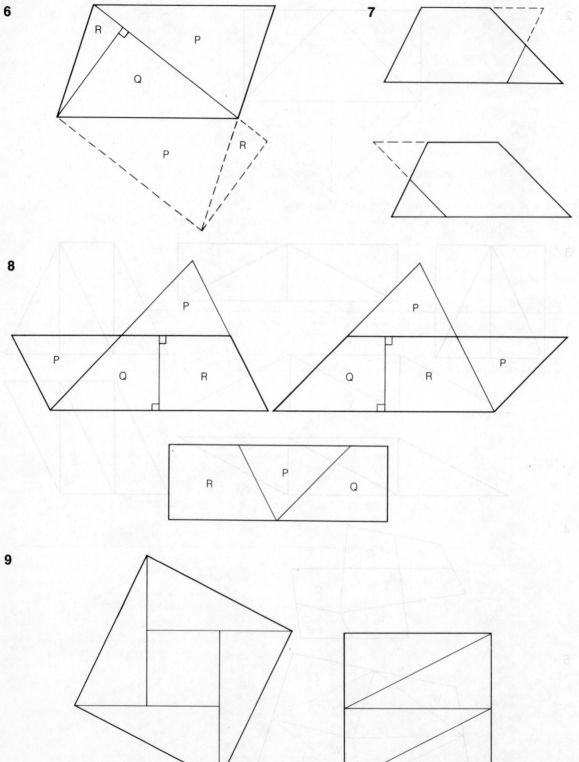

10

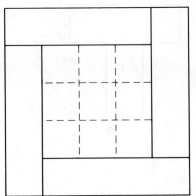

11

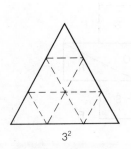

3^2

$+$

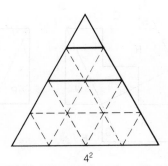

4^2

$=$

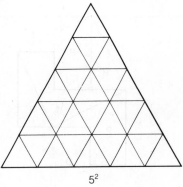

5^2

12

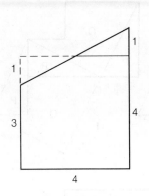

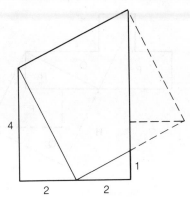

13

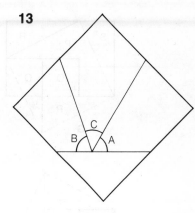

14

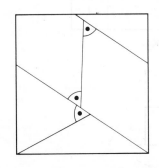

15

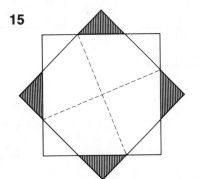

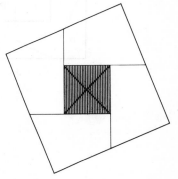

16

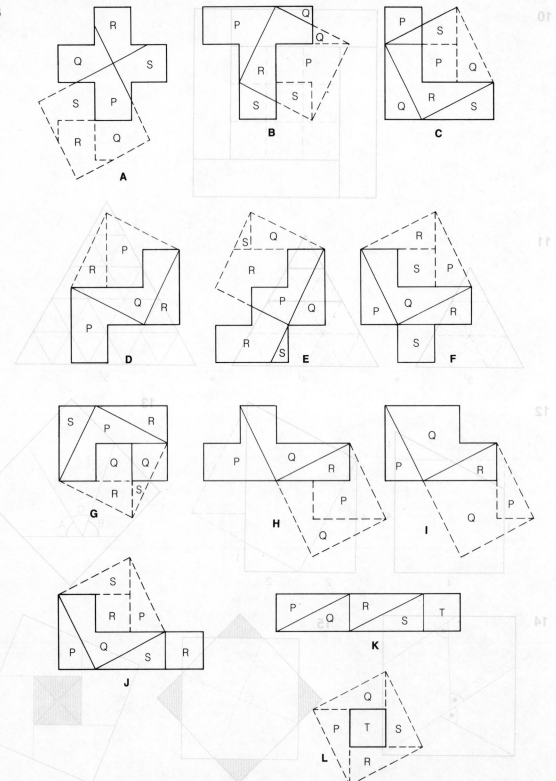

17

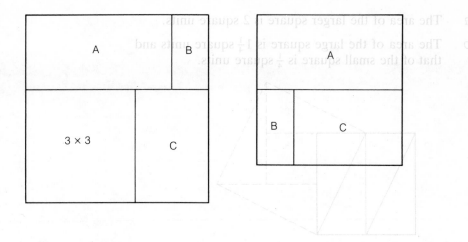

18

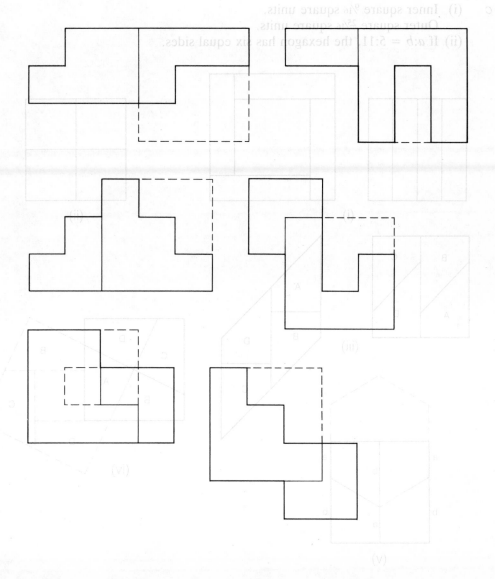

19 *a*   The area of the larger square is 2 square units.

   b   The area of the large square is $1\frac{1}{4}$ square units and
        that of the small square is $\frac{1}{4}$ square units.

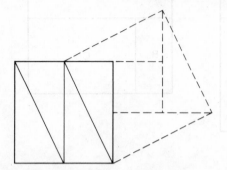

   c   (i) Inner square $\frac{9}{16}$ square units.
             Outer square $\frac{25}{16}$ square units.
        (ii) If $a{:}b = 5{:}11$, the hexagon has six equal sides.

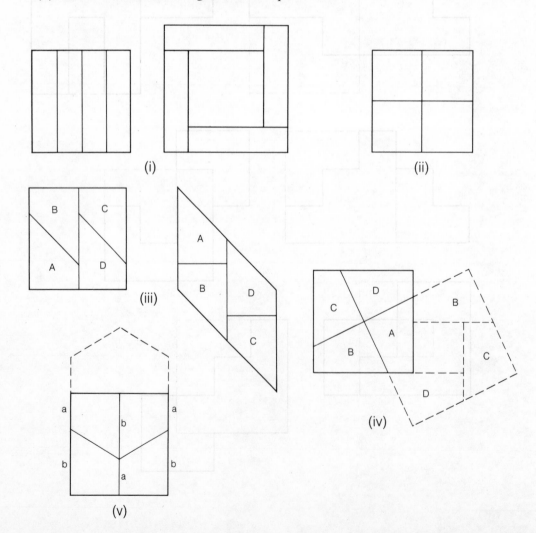

20

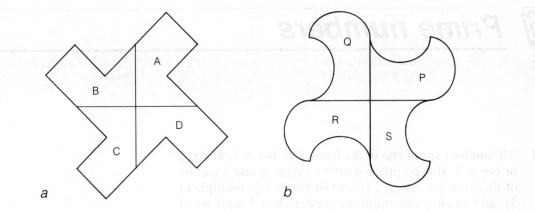

a

b

6 *Prime numbers*

Q1 All numbers are of one of the forms $6m$, $6m \pm 1$, $6m \pm 2$ or $6m \pm 3$. But no prime number except 2 and 3 can be of the form $6m$, $6m \pm 2$ (even) or $6m \pm 3$ (a multiple of 3), and so all prime numbers greater than 3 must be of the form $6m - 1$ or $6m + 1$.

Q2 The squares of all prime numbers greater than 5 have 1 or 9 as their final digit, and all squares of prime numbers greater than 3 are of the form $24m + 1$.

Q3 $(6m - 1)(6m + 1) + 1 = 36m^2 = (6m)^2$.

Q4 $n^2 - n + 11$ produces ten prime numbers for values of n from 1 to 10, but composite numbers when $n = 11$ or 12. Some higher values of n also produce prime numbers.

Q5 $n^2 - n + 17$ produces a sequence of 16 prime numbers. $n^2 - n + 41$ produces a sequence of 40 prime numbers.

Q6 A formula such as $An^3 + Bn^2 + Cn + p$ where p is any number, however large, produces a multiple of p when $n = p$. If p is a prime number, a formula might be found that produces a sequence of $p - 1$ prime numbers.

Q7 The formula produces the sequence 1, 7, 19, 37, 61, 91, 127, 169; the first five are prime numbers and $n = 8$ produces the first square, $169 = 13^2$. $n = 6$ produces the composite number 91.

Q8 For example: $4n^2 + 7$ which produces seven prime numbers when $n = 0 - 6$, and $4n^2 + 37$ which produces nine prime numbers.

Q9 $2n^2 + p$ when $p = 5$ produces a sequence of five prime numbers, when $p = 11$ a sequence of 11 prime numbers, but other values of p do not produce sequences until $p = 29$, which produces no less than 29 prime numbers.

Q10 $4n^2 + 37$ produces a sequence of nine prime numbers, and $6n^2 + 7$ produces a sequence of 7.

Q11 Each of these formulae produces a sequence of prime numbers.

Q12

2n	2	4	6	8	10	12	14	16	18	20	22	24	26	28
P(2n)	1	2	2	2	2	2	3	2	3	3	3	4	3	2

Q13 $30 = 1 + 29 = 7 + 23 = 11 + 19 = 13 + 17$, and each prime number in the range from 15 to 30 can be paired with one in the range from 1 to 15, and so $P(30) = 4$ is a MAX.
Note: although $P(34) = 4$ it is not a MAX, since 19 has no prime number in the range from 1 to 17 with which it can be paired.

Q14 In the range from 32 to 48 there are MAXs only when $2n = 36, 42, 48$, which are multiples of 6.

Q15 $P(2n)$ increases irregularly as $2n$ increases. It appears that 28 is the largest number for which $P(2n)$ is 2, and that $P(2n)$ is greater than 2 when $2n$ is greater than 28.

Q16 15 even numbers less than 50 are 1 more than a prime number and 9 are not.

Q17 1, 7, 13, 19, 31, 37, 43, 61, 67, 73, 79, 97 are 1 more than a multiple of 6, and 5, 11, 17, 23, 29, 41, 47, 53, 59, 71, 83, 89 are 1 less than a multiple of 6. There are twelve of each of the forms $6m + 1$ and $6m - 1$ less than 100. There are approximately the same number of each form as the total number of primes increases.

Q18 Even numbers that are multiples of 3 have greater values for $P(2n)$ than their neighbours $P(2n - 2)$ and $P(2n + 2)$, and their peaks in the graph are becoming more prominent.

Q19 $92 = 2^2 \times 23$, $98 = 2 \times 7^2$, $122 = 2 \times 61$, $128 = 2^7$, all of which have only one or two prime factors, whereas $96 = 2^5 \times 3$, $102 = 2 \times 3 \times 17$, $108 = 2^2 \times 3^3$, $114 = 2 \times 3 \times 19$, $120 = 2^3 \times 3 \times 5$, all of which have two or more prime factors including 3, and 120 also has the small prime factor 5.

Q20 $P(90)$, $P(120)$ and $P(210)$ produce a MAX, and the others are 'near misses', as $150 = 49 + 101$, $180 = 77 + 103$, $240 = 49 + 191$, $270 = 77 + 193$.

Q21 $210 = 1 \times 2 \times 3 \times 5 \times 7$, the product of the five smallest prime numbers, and $420 = 1 \times 2^2 \times 3 \times 5 \times 7$. But P(420) is not a MAX, since $420 = 143 + 277 = 169 + 251 = 187 + 233$.

Q22 Consider first the even numbers that have 3 as a factor (as the graph shows, these have higher values of P(2n) than their neighbours), and investigate the sum of pairs of prime numbers less than 100. There are 12 primes of the form $6n - 1$, which when added in pairs produce 78 even numbers of the form $6n - 2$. When each is added to 3, 12 even numbers of the form $6n + 2$ are produced.

Similarly pairs of numbers of the form $6n + 1$ produce 78 even numbers of the form $6n + 2$, and 12 of the form $6n + 4$ (the same form as $6n - 2$) when 3 is added to each.

But when a number of the form $6n - 1$ is added to one of the form $6n + 1$ no less than 144 even numbers of the form $6m$ are produced. This is many more than the $78 + 12 = 90$ produced in each of the $6n - 2$ and $6n + 2$ forms. This shows that pairs of prime numbers in the range from 1 to 97 produce more even numbers that are multiples of 6 than those of the form $6n - 2$ or $6n + 2$: 144, 90 and 90 respectively.

The preponderance of multiples of 6 increases when the range of prime numbers is from 1 to 199, and in general, when we take the first M primes of the form $6n - 1$ and the first M primes of the form $6n + 1$, we find that M^2 even numbers of the form $6m$ are produced, and only $\frac{1}{2}M(M + 3)$ in each of the forms $6n - 2$ and $6n + 2$. The difference between M^2 and $\frac{1}{2}M(M + 3)$ is $\frac{1}{2}M(M - 3)$, which is positive when M is greater than 3, and it increases rapidly as M increases. This explains why the peaks at P(6n) become more prominent as 2n increases.

Prime numbers less than 100 can also be segregated into five sets:

those of the form $5m + 1$: 1, 11, 31, 41, 61, 71
those of the form $5m + 2$: 2, 7, 17, 37, 47, 67, 97
those of the form $5m + 3$: 3, 13, 23, 43, 53, 73, 83
those of the form $5m + 4$: 19, 29, 59, 79, 89
and the only one of the form $5m$: 5

When pairs of these primes are added together, they produce 73 even numbers of the form $10m$, 56 of the form $10m + 2$, 68 of the form $10m + 4$, 63 of the form $10m + 6$, and 58 of the form $10m + 8$. This shows that a few more multiples of 10 are produced than even numbers in the other sets but, if we consider prime numbers less than 200, they produce 254 multiples of 10, and an average of less than 200 even numbers in each of the other forms.

Problems

1   Four primes appear in the second row of the square.

2   Even numbers appear in alternate columns of the square.

3   Multiples of 5 appear in the fifth and tenth columns.

4   Multiples of 4 have been blacked out, forming a knight's move pattern.
Multiples of 6 also form a knight's move pattern.

5   Multiples of 3 lie on diagonal lines sloping downwards to the left — a bishop's move pattern.

6   Multiples of 9 and 11 also lie on diagonal lines.

7   The prime numbers left in the square after deleting multiples of 2, 3, 5 and 7 are

1	2	3	5	7	
11		13		17	19
		23			29
31				37	
41		43		47	
		53			59
61				67	
71		73			79
		83			89
				97	

The prime numbers do not form a regular pattern, but apart from 2 and 5 in the first row, all other primes have 1, 3, 7 or 9 as their final digit. The chart also shows that there are several pairs of primes that differ by 10 in each column, but only 3, 13, 23 form an arithmetic progression with a common difference of 10. It also shows that all primes greater than 3 are either 1 less or 1 more than a multiple of 6.

8   There are 26 primes and 74 composite numbers.

9   The values of $n^2 + n + 5$ are 5, 7, 11, 17, 25, 35, 47, 61, 77, of which six are primes and three are composite numbers.

10 $24 = 1 + 23 = 5 + 19 = 7 + 17 = 11 + 13$ 4 ways
$26 = 3 + 23 = 7 + 19 = 13 + 13$ 3 ways
$28 = 5 + 23 = 11 + 17$ 2 ways
$30 = 1 + 29 = 7 + 23 = 11 + 19 = 13 + 17$ 4 ways
$32 = 1 + 31 = 3 + 29 = 13 + 19$ 3 ways
$34 = 3 + 31 = 5 + 29 = 11 + 23 = 17 + 17$ 4 ways
$36 = 5 + 31 = 7 + 29 = 13 + 23 = 17 + 19$ 4 ways

All even numbers in the range from 24 to 36 can be expressed as the sum of two prime numbers in two, three or four ways.

11 $5^2 = 25 = 24 + 1$
$7^2 = 49 = 24 \times 2 + 1$
$11^2 = 121 = 24 \times 5 + 1$
$13^2 = 169 = 24 \times 7 + 1$

The remainder after division by 24 is always 1.
When the prime number is of the form $6n - 1$, its square is $36n^2 - 12n + 1 = 12n(n - 3) + 1$. But $n(n - 3)$ is always even, since either n or $n - 3$ is even. So $36n^2 - 12n + 1$, and similarly $(6n + 1)^2$, leaves a remainder 1 after division by 24. All primes greater than 3 are of the form $6n - 1$ or $6n + 1$.

12   If $m^2 - n^2 = p$, then $(m - n)(m + n) = 1 \times p$ where p is an odd prime number greater than 2. Then if $m - n = 1$ and $m + n = p$, $2m = p + 1$ and $2n = p - 1$. Both $p - 1$ and $p + 1$ are even numbers, and so $m = \frac{1}{2}(p + 1)$ and $n = \frac{1}{2}(p - 1)$ are both positive integers.

13 $5 = 1^2 + 2^2$, $13 = 2^2 + 3^2$, $17 = 1^2 + 4^2$

and

$5^2 = 25 = 3^2 + 4^2$, $13^2 = 169 = 5^2 + 12^2$,
$17^2 = 289 = 8^2 + 15^2$.

14 $1 + 5 \times 7 = 1 + 35 = 36 = 6^2$
$1 + 11 \times 13 = 1 + 143 = 12^2$
$1 + 17 \times 19 = 1 + 323 = 18^2$
$1 + 29 \times 31 = 1 + 899 = 30^2$
$1 + 41 \times 43 = 1 + 1763 = 42^2$
$1 + 59 \times 61 = 1 + 3599 = 60^2$

The result is always the square of a multiple of 6, because $(6n - 1)(6n + 1) = (6n)^2 - 1$. The only exceptions are the pairs (1,3) and (3,5), which produce 2^2 and 4^2.

15   Multiples of 3 lie on diagonal lines.
Multiples of 5 form a knight's move pattern.
Multiples of 7 appear in the middle column.

Multiples of 13 form a knight's move pattern.
Prime numbers less than 200 are shown in this table:

1	3	5	7		11	13
	17	19		23		27
29	31			37		41
43		47			53	
	59	61			67	
71	73			79		83
		89				97
	101	103		107	109	
113						
127		131			137	139
				149	151	
	157			163		167
		173			179	181
				191	193	
197	199					

7 Knight's tours

Q1 If a knight starts on a white square, it can move only to a black square, and the second move will take it to another white square. Hence all the odd-numbered squares will be white, and all the even-numbered squares will be black.

Q2

1	24	13	18	7
14	19	8	23	12
9	2	25	6	17
20	15	4	11	22
3	10	21	16	5

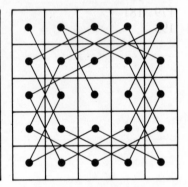

One of several knight's tours on a 5-by-5 board is shown above. The first and last squares are numbered 1 and 25, which are both odd, and therefore are on squares of the same colour and so the knight cannot move from one to the other and make a unicursal route diagram.

Q3

	12	7	2	
6	1		13	8
11				3
	5		9	
	10		4	

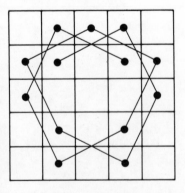

The squares numbered 8–13 must be reflections in the line of symmetry of the squares numbered 6, 5, 4, 3, 2, 1.

Q4

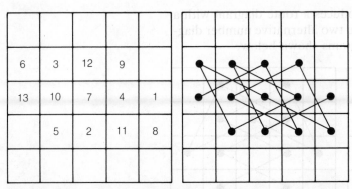

The first and last squares, numbered 1 and 13, must be reflections of each other in the line of symmetry. Similarly the square numbered 2 must be a reflection of the square numbered 12; in general, squares whose numbers average 7 are reflections of each other, and the square numbered 7 must be on a line of symmetry, where it is its own reflection.

Q5

If a black-and-white pattern of a knight's tour has rotational symmetry only, the central square must contain the number 7, and pairs of squares with numbers that average 7 must be on a line through the central cell and equidistant from it.

Problems

1   The pattern has four lines of symmetry.

2   *a*   The knight's two-move pattern has eight black squares, with four lines of symmetry.

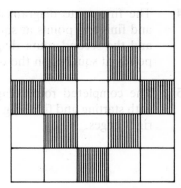

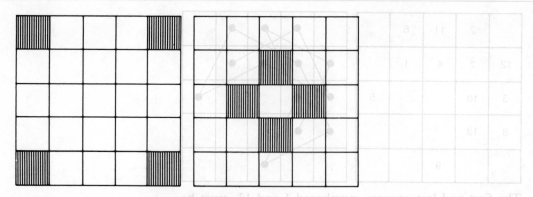

b   The knight's three-move pattern has four black squares, with four lines of symmetry.

c   The four-move pattern also has four black squares, with four lines of symmetry.

3   The numbered diagram produces a route diagram with a single line of symmetry. The two alternative number diagrams lead to the route diagrams shown below.

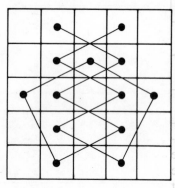 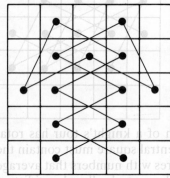

4   The first route diagram can be completed with starting and finishing points at squares on the top and left edges, and the second route diagram has starting and finishing points at squares on the other two edges.

5   The completed route diagram has rotational symmetry, with starting and finishing points at squares on the left and right edges.

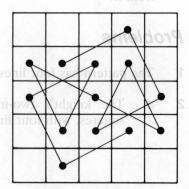

6   One of the route diagrams with a pattern symmetrical about the central line is shown below, together with a route diagram with rotational symmetry, and the beginning of another route diagram with rotational symmetry.

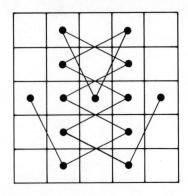 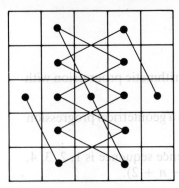 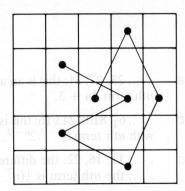

7

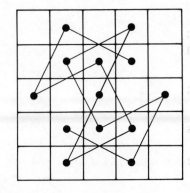 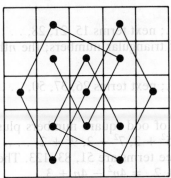

8

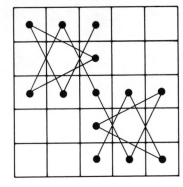 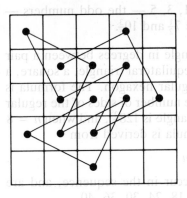

9   There is no symmetrical route diagram for the black-and-white pattern with a single line of symmetry.

8 *What comes next?*

Q1 *a*   . . ., 23, 27, 31: this is an arithmetic progression with nth term $4n + 3$.

   b   . . ., $6\frac{3}{4}$, 81/8, 243/16: this is a geometrical progression with nth term $3^{n-1}/2^{n-2}$.

   c   . . ., 11, 16, 22: the difference sequence is 1, 2, 3, 4, . . .; the nth term is $\frac{1}{2}(n^2 - n + 2)$.

Q2 PASTE—PASTEL; PRATE—PIRATE; PATEN—PATENT.

Q3 *a*   Differences 2, 3, 4, . . .; next terms 15, 21, 28, . . .; this is the sequence of triangular numbers; the nth term is $\frac{1}{2}n(n + 1)$.

   b   Differences 3, 5, 7, . . .; next terms 26, 37, 50, . . .; nth term $n^2 + 1$.

   c   The sequence is made of odd square numbers plus 2, i.e. $1^2 + 2$, $3^2 + 2$, $5^2 + 2$, $7^2 + 2$, $9^2 + 2$, ... Therefore the next three terms are 51, 83, 123. The nth term is $(2n - 1)^2 + 2 = 4n^2 - 4n + 3$.

Q4 See **Q1** and **Q3** above.

Q5 The first three terms are 1, 3, 5 — the odd numbers — but the next two terms are $7\frac{1}{2}$ and $10\frac{3}{5}$.

Q6 The sequence shows the angle in degrees between a pair of consecutive sides of an equilateral triangle, a square, a regular pentagon and a regular hexagon. The formula is $180(n - 2)/n$ where n is the number of sides of the regular polygon. When $n = 7$, the angle is $128\frac{2}{7}^{\circ}$, and when $n = 8$ the angle is 135°. The formula is derived from

$$180 - 360/n = 180(n - 2)/n$$

All the numbers shown occur in the sequence, and are produced when $n = 9, 12, 18, 24, 30, 36, 40$.

Q7 The differences sequence is $2An + A + B$, which produces an arithmetic progression with $3A + B$ as its first term and common difference $2A$.

Q8 9/13, 11/16, 13/19. The *n*th term is $(2n + 1)/(3n + 1)$, the numerators and denominators forming arithmetic progressions.

$3/4 - 5/7 = 1/28, 5/7 - 7/10 = 1/70, 7/10 - 9/13 = 1/130$

The differences in the sequence are all positive and have 1 as their numerator, showing that the first fraction 3/4 is the largest and that each subsequent fraction is less than the previous one. But every fraction is greater than 2/3, since $(2n + 1)/(3n + 1) - 2/3 = 1/3(3n + 1)$.

Q9 All you need in order to calculate the radii of these diminishing circles is to apply Pythagoras' theorem.

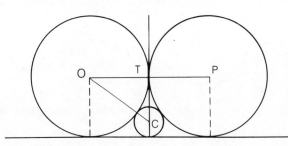
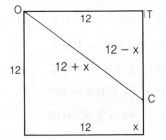

If *x* is the radius of the third circle, centre C, then △OTC has a right-angle at T, OT = 12, OC = 12 + *x*, TC = 12 − *x*. OC^2 = OT^2 + TC^2, i.e.

$$(12 + x)^2 = 12^2 + (12 - x)^2$$

and hence *x* = 3. If *y* is the radius of the fourth circle, centre D, then OT = 12, OD = 12 + *y*, TD = 6 − *y*, and

$$(12 + y)^2 = 12^2 + (6 - y)^2$$

and so *y* = 1. If *z* is the radius of the fifth circle, centre E, OT = 12, OE = 12 + *z*, TE = 4 − *z*, then

$$(12 + z)^2 = 12^2 + (4 - z)^2$$

and so $z = \frac{1}{2}$.

The sequence is 12, 3, 1, $\frac{1}{2}$, . . ., and further circles have radii that can be calculated by this method. The triangles OTC, OTD, OTE have sides in the ratios (3, 4, 5), (5, 12, 13), (7, 24, 25), and the next in this sequence will be (9, 40, 41), (11, 60, 61) etc. which are the Pythagorean solutions to $a^2 + b^2 = c^2$.

Problems

1 Four-eighths, ⁴⁄₈; eight-sixteenths, ⁸⁄₁₆.

2 Three-ninths, ³⁄₉; four-twelfths, ⁴⁄₁₂.

3 Equivalent fractions:

   a $\frac{1}{2} = \frac{3}{6} = \frac{6}{12} = \frac{5}{10} = \frac{11}{22}$

   b $\frac{2}{3} = \frac{4}{6} = \frac{6}{9} = \frac{6}{9} = \frac{10}{15}$

   c $\frac{3}{4} = \frac{6}{8} = \frac{9}{12} = \frac{18}{24} = \frac{27}{36}$

4 *a*   Black, $\frac{6}{16} = \frac{3}{8}$; white, $\frac{10}{16} = \frac{5}{8}$.

   b   Black, $\frac{7}{20}$; white, $\frac{13}{20}$.

   c   Black, $\frac{10}{24} = \frac{5}{12}$; white, $\frac{14}{24} = \frac{7}{12}$.

5 *a* $\frac{1}{2} = 0.5 = 50\%$

   b $\frac{6}{10} = \frac{3}{5} = 0.6 = 60\%$

   c $\frac{1}{1} = 1 = 100\%$

   d $\frac{1}{1} = 1 = 100\%$

   e $\frac{3}{5} = 0.6 = 60\%$

   f $\frac{4}{2} = 2 = 200\%$

6 *a* $x = 10$, $y = 15$.

   b $z = 35$, $w = 35$, $u = 49$.

       If $x/y = \frac{3}{4}$, then $x = 3m$ and $y = 4m$. Substitute these values for x and y in each of the fractions, and it simplifies to $\frac{3}{4}$, so that each fraction is equivalent to $\frac{3}{4}$.

7 *a*   In this patterned sequence of fractions of the form $(2n + 1)/(3n + 1)$, each fraction is followed by a larger fraction. $\frac{9}{13}$ is followed by putting $n = 5$, producing $\frac{11}{16}$. So $\frac{3}{4}$ is the least, and $(2n + 1)/(3n + 1)$ is greater than the first four fractions, when n is greater than 4.

   b $\frac{4}{7}$ (and any other proper fraction) increases when the same positive number is added to numerator and denominator, and diminishes when a number is subtracted. $(4m + 1)/(7m + 1)$ also is greater than $\frac{4}{7}$.

   c $\frac{31}{100} = 0.31$, $\frac{33}{110} = 0.30$, $\frac{37}{111} = 0.\dot{3}$, so $\frac{33}{110} = \frac{3}{10}$ is the least and $\frac{37}{111} = \frac{1}{3}$ is the greatest of the three fractions.

8

```
              1    2
           1    3    2
         1    4    5    2
       1    5    9    7    2
     1    6   14   16    9    2
   1    7   20   30   25   11    2
```

$$\text{Sum } 3 = 3 \times \ \ 1 = 3 \times 2^0$$
$$6 = 3 \times \ \ 2 = 3 \times 2^1$$
$$12 = 3 \times \ \ 4 = 3 \times 2^2$$
$$24 = 3 \times \ \ 8 = 3 \times 2^3$$
$$48 = 3 \times 16 = 3 \times 2^4$$
$$96 = 3 \times 32 = 3 \times 2^5$$

a

n	1	2	3	4	5
$\frac{1}{2}(3n)$	$1\frac{1}{2}$	3	$4\frac{1}{2}$	6	$7\frac{1}{2}$
$\frac{1}{2}n^2$	$\frac{1}{2}$	2	$4\frac{1}{2}$	8	$12\frac{1}{2}$
$\frac{1}{2}n(n+3)$	2	5	9	14	20

b   1, 3, 5, 7, 9, 11 is the sequence of odd numbers. The formula for the nth term is $2n - 1$.

c   1, 4, 9, 16, 25 is the sequence of square numbers, n^2.

d   1, 5, 14, 30 is the sequence 1^2, $1^2 + 2^2$, $1^2 + 2^2 + 3^2$, $1^2 + 2^2 + 3^2 + 4^2$.

e   See table of sums above. The sum of the numbers in the nth row is $3 \times 2^{n-1}$.

f
$$\qquad\qquad 2 \quad\ 7 \quad\ 16 \quad 30 \quad (50) \quad (77)$$
first differences $\quad\ 5 \quad\ 9 \quad\ 14 \quad (20) \quad (27)$
second differences $\qquad 4 \quad\ 5 \quad (6) \quad\ (7)$

Assuming that the second differences are the sequence of natural numbers, it will continue as shown above, and so the sequence of first differences can be calculated, and hence the original sequence can be continued. The formula for the nth term is $n(n + 1)(n + 5)/6$.

9 More magic square patterns

Q1 The sums of the numbers in the top and bottom rows are the same, 101, and the sums of the numbers in the first and third columns are the same, 89, both of which are prime numbers. The sums in the other row and column are also primes, 83 and 107, but the sums of the numbers in both diagonals are composite numbers, 77 and 93.

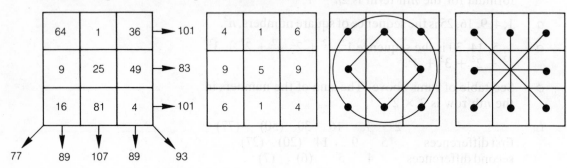

Q2 Both patterns shown above have four lines of symmetry.

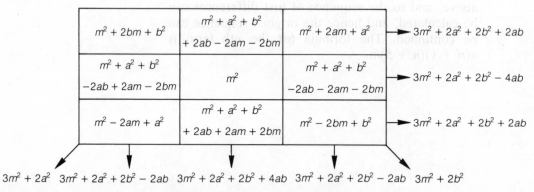

$m^2 + 2bm + b^2$	$m^2 + a^2 + b^2 + 2ab - 2am - 2bm$	$m^2 + 2am + a^2$ → $3m^2 + 2a^2 + 2b^2 + 2ab$
$m^2 + a^2 + b^2 -2ab + 2am - 2bm$	m^2	$m^2 + a^2 + b^2 -2ab - 2am - 2bm$ → $3m^2 + 2a^2 + 2b^2 - 4ab$
$m^2 - 2am + a^2$	$m^2 + a^2 + b^2 + 2ab + 2am + 2bm$	$m^2 - 2bm + b^2$ → $3m^2 + 2a^2 + 2b^2 + 2ab$

$3m^2 + 2a^2$ $3m^2 + 2a^2 + 2b^2 - 2ab$ $3m^2 + 2a^2 + 2b^2 + 4ab$ $3m^2 + 2a^2 + 2b^2 - 2ab$ $3m^2 + 2b^2$

Q3 The diagram shows that in every 3-by-3 magic square the sums of the squares of the numbers in the top and bottom rows are the same, and that the sums of the squares of the numbers in the first and third columns are the same.

Q4 The products of the numbers in the rows are 48, 105, 72, whose sum is $225 = 15^2$, and the products of the numbers in the columns are 96, 45, 84, whose sum is also $225 = 15^2$. The products of the numbers in the diagonals are 80 and 120, whose sum is 200.

Q5

2	1	6
7	5	3
4	9	8

The square formed by the final digits of the cubes of the numbers in the Chinese magic square, shown here, contains the numbers from 1 to 9, but it is not magic. The pattern formed by linking pairs of numbers whose sum is 10 is the same as in the Chinese magic square, and as in the fourth diagram above for **Q1**. It has the same sequences in its diagonals, middle row and central column as the Chinese magic square.

Q6 The sum of each set of four numbers is 34.

Q7

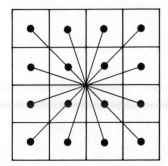

Q8 The sum of each set of numbers in the four corner cells and in the four central cells is 34. This is the same as the sum of the numbers in the cells marked R and in those marked S.

Q9 The sum of the four numbers in each of the corners is 34.

Q10 The pattern has a central line of symmetry.

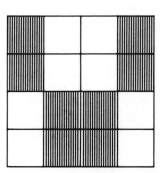

Q11 The pattern has a diagonal line of symmetry.

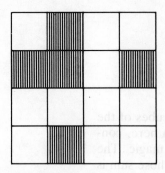

Q12 The pattern has a diagonal line of symmetry.

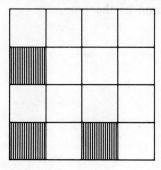

Q13 The pattern has rotational symmetry.

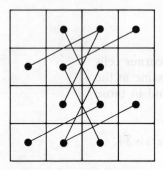

Q14 The pattern has two lines of symmetry.

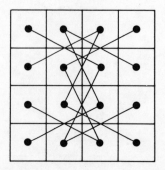

Q15

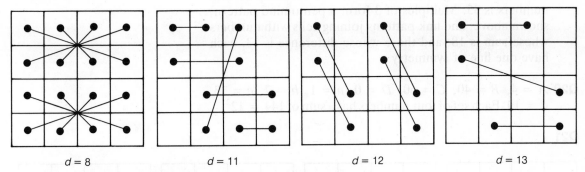

$d = 8$ $d = 11$ $d = 12$ $d = 13$

The link diagram joining cells whose numbers differ by 8 has two lines of symmetry, whereas those with differences of 11, 12 and 13 have rotational symmetry.

Q16 The completion of Figure 7 is shown by letters in Figure 8.

Q17 The sum of each set of four numbers is $(A + B + C + D) + (a + b + c + d)$.

Q18

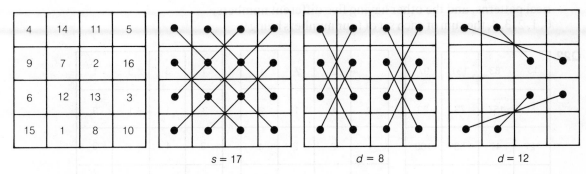

4	14	11	5
9	7	2	16
6	12	13	3
15	1	8	10

$s = 17$ $d = 8$ $d = 12$

This 4-by-4 magic square made with the numbers from 1 to 16 has different diagrams linking cells with numbers whose sum is 17, or whose differences are 8 or 12.

Q19

1	10	16	8
7	17	9	2
12	3	6	14
15	5	4	11

$3m$ $s = 18$ $d = 13$

This 4-by-4 magic square is made with the numbers from 1 to 17, omitting 13, and the sum of each set of four numbers is 35. Multiples of 3 form a pentomino pattern, shown above, and link patterns joining cells with numbers whose sum is 18, and those whose difference is 13, each have one line of symmetry.

Q20 $A = 4$, $B = 40$, $C = 60$, $D = 0$, $a = 1$, $b = 7$, $c = 13$, $d = 19$. Each set of four numbers has a sum of $144 = 12^2$.

Q21

2	1	1	2
2	1	1	2
1	2	2	1
1	2	2	1

1	3	1	3
1	3	1	3
3	1	3	1
3	1	3	1

0	2	3	4
3	4	1	1
4	2	2	1
2	1	3	3

5	1	1	5
5	1	1	5
1	5	5	1
1	5	5	1

All the remainder patterns are magic squares, three of them having only two different numbers that form symmetrical patterns, and the other having five different numbers, 0, 1, 2, 3, 4, the sum of each set of four numbers being 9.

Q22

13	83	131	97
71	157	73	23
127	41	53	103
113	43	67	101

1	2	2	1
2	1	1	2
1	2	2	1
2	1	1	2

1	3	3	1
3	1	1	3
3	1	1	3
1	3	3	1

3	3	1	2
1	2	3	3
2	1	3	3
3	3	2	1

1	5	5	1
5	1	1	5
1	5	5	1
5	1	1	5

By choosing $(A, B, C, D) = (0, 30, 60, 90)$ and $(a, b, c, d) = (13, 23, 41, 67)$, the above all-prime magic square is obtained, and its remainder patterns are all magic squares.

Q23 $(A, B, C, D, E) = (20, 15, 10, 5, 0)$, $(a, b, c, d, e) = (1, 2, 3, 4, 5)$. Each set of five numbers have a sum of 65.

Q24 The black-and-white pattern has rotational symmetry.

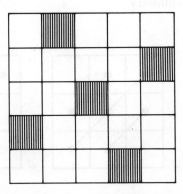

Q25

1	263	59	127	17
83	73	11	31	269
41	37	293	29	67
239	23	97	47	61
103	71	7	233	53

1	3	4	2	2
3	3	1	1	4
1	2	3	4	2
4	3	2	2	1
3	1	2	3	3

This 5-by-5 magic square contains 25 prime numbers.
The remainders after division by 5 produce a magic square made with the numbers 1, 2, 3, 4, in which the sum of each set of five numbers is 12.
The remainders after division by 3 and 6 also produce magic squares, but with only two different numbers in each.

Problems

1 Cells containing numbers that differ by 4 make a pattern
with two lines of symmetry:

    a   two lines of symmetry and rotational symmetry

    b   rotational symmetry only

    c   two lines of symmetry and rotational symmetry

    d   rotational symmetry only.

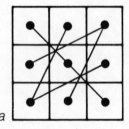 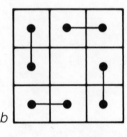 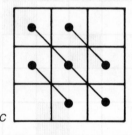 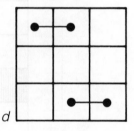

a   *b*   *c*   *d*

2

4	3	8
9	5	1
2	7	6

6	7	2
1	5	9
8	3	4

2	9	4
7	5	3
6	1	8

Multiples of the numbers in the Chinese magic square by
3, 7, or 9 also form magic squares. The squares formed
by their final digits are the same as the original Chinese
magic square, with the numbers from 1 to 4 and 6 to 9 in
alternative positions.

3

10	1	7
3	6	9
5	11	2

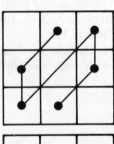

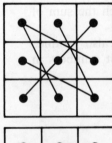

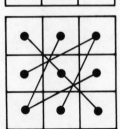

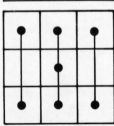

All the difference patterns have two lines of symmetry and/or rotational symmetry.

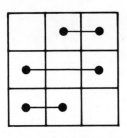 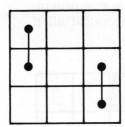 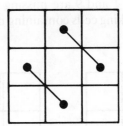 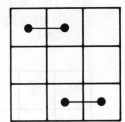

2	1	3
3	2	1
1	3	2

The remainders after division by 4 make a magic square with the numbers 1, 2, 3 only.

4 The sums of the numbers in the top and bottom rows are the same, 150, and the sums of the numbers in left and right sides of the square are the same, 134.
The remainders after division by 4 do not make a magic square, but form a symmetrical black-and-white pattern.

100	1	49
9	36	81
25	121	4

0	1	1
1	0	1
1	1	0

5

$2a + b$	0	$a + 2b$
$2b$	$a + b$	$2a$
a	$2a+2b$	b

7	0	5
2	4	6
3	8	1

8	0	7
4	5	6
3	10	2

a The sum of the numbers in each row, column and diagonal is $3(a + b)$.

b The magic square is made with the numbers from 0 to 8.

c When one is added to each number, the Chinese magic square is formed.

d The numbers 1 and 9 are missing but a new pattern is made by linking cells containing numbers that differ by 1.

6

10	15	5	4
8	1	11	14
3	6	16	9
13	12	2	7

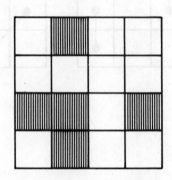

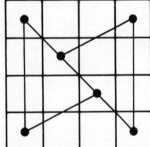
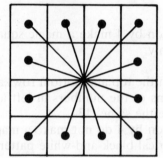

a 0 + 4 + 8 + 12 + 1 + 2 + 3 + 4 = 34, which is the sum of each set of four numbers in rows, columns and diagonals.

b The pattern has a single line of symmetry.

c The link pattern has rotational symmetry only.

d The link pattern has four lines of symmetry.

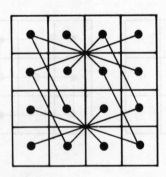
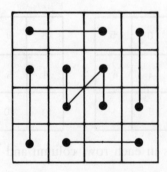
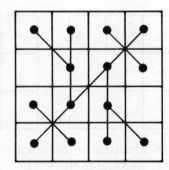

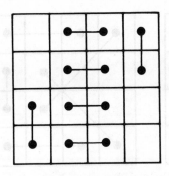
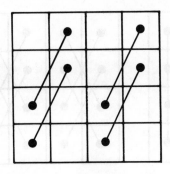

e   All the difference patterns have rotational symmetry.
Only those for differences of 4, 5, 9, 10 and 12 are
shown above.

7

2	16	11	5
9	7	4	14
8	10	13	3
15	1	6	12

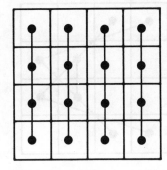
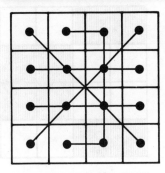

a   The sum is 34 in each row, column and diagonal.

b   The sum is 34 in each of the sets of four cells marked
P, Q, R, S, X, Y, Z, W.

c   There is one diagonal line of symmetry.

d   Pairs whose sum is 17 lie in columns, making a pattern
with two lines of symmetry.

e

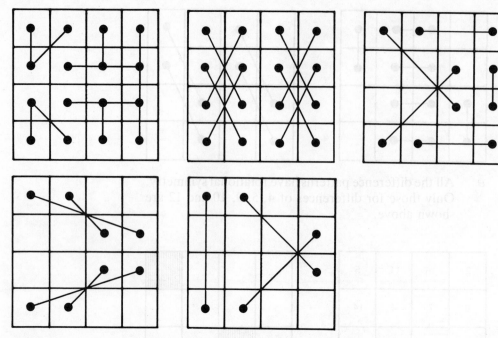

They all have a horizontal line of symmetry, but when the difference is 8 the pattern also has a vertical line of symmetry.

8

13	83	131	97
71	157	73	23
127	41	53	103
113	43	67	101

a   All sixteen numbers are prime numbers.

b   The black-and-white pattern has a single line of symmetry.

c   The pattern has a single line of symmetry.

d   The sum of each set of four numbers is $324 = 4 \times 81 = 2^2 \times 3^4$, a square number with two prime factors.

e   All difference patterns have a single line of symmetry, like those for $d = 10$ and $d = 60$ shown above.

f

1	2	2	1
2	1	1	2
1	2	2	1
2	1	1	2

1	3	3	1
3	1	1	3
3	1	1	3
1	3	3	1

3	3	1	2
1	2	3	3
2	1	3	3
3	3	2	1

1	5	5	1
5	1	1	5
1	5	5	1
5	1	1	5

Three of the remainder squares are magic, but the pattern after division by 4 is not, although it makes a symmetrical black-and-white pattern with four lines of symmetry. The sum of the numbers in each row and column is 8, but in the diagonals it is 4.

g   (i) $13 + 131 = 71 + 73 = 41 + 103 = 43 + 101$
          $= 144$.
     (ii) $23 + 157 = 53 + 127 = 67 + 113 = 83 + 97$
          $= 180$.

Both link diagrams form patterns with rotational symmetry.

9

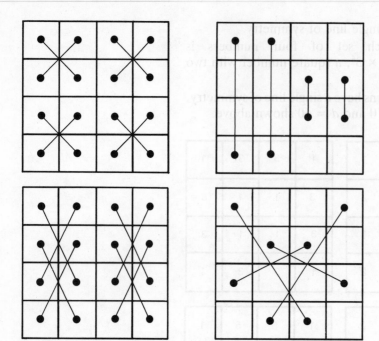

a $A = 0$, $b = 12$, $C = 8$, $D = 4$, $a = 4$, $b = 1$, $c = 2$, $d = 3$.

b   The above patterns have respectively 4, 1, 2, 1 lines of symmetry.

c

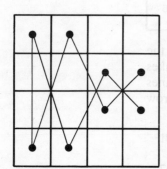 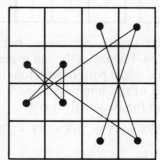

The above patterns have a single line of symmetry.

d   Numbers in the left-hand columns have a difference of 2: those in the right-hand columns have a difference of 6. Numbers in the two top rows have a difference of 7, and those in the two bottom rows have a difference of 9.

Q10

22	11	9	5	18
4	20	23	12	6
13	7	1	19	25
16	24	15	8	2
10	3	17	21	14

a

b

a   The sum is always 65.

b   The black-and-white pattern has two lines of symmetry.

c   The link patterns joining
   (i)   pairs of odd numbers whose sum is 26,
   (ii) pairs of even numbers whose sum is 26,
   (iii) pairs whose difference is 12,
have each a single line of symmetry.

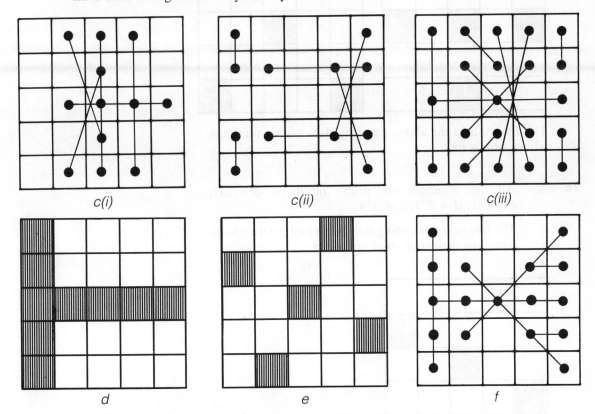

c(i)   *c(ii)*   *c(iii)*

d   *e*   *f*

d   The numbers that are one more than a multiple of 3
    are 1, 4, 7, 10, 13, 16, 19, 22, 25 which all lie in the
    first column or in the middle row.

e   1, 2, 3, 4, 5 form a pattern with rotational symmetry.

f   The four sequences make a pattern with one line of symmetry. The other arithmetic progressions with common difference 6, i.e. (3, 9, 15, 21) and 5, 11, 17, 23), do not make symmetrical link patterns, but do make symmetrical black-and-white patterns.

11   Each set of five cells forming the St. George's cross pattern contain numbers whose sum is 65. The nine possible positions for the cross have one of the nine central cells at its centre.

12   There are nine corresponding positions for five cells forming the domino pattern for 5, and each set contains numbers whose sum is 65.

13

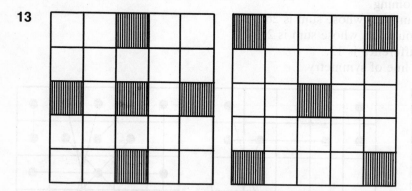

The five cells in the above patterns also contain numbers whose sum is 65.

14   *a*   All the numbers are prime numbers: $b = 137$, $c = 151$, $d = 277$; $e = 329$.

b   The five cells containing numbers ending with 9 form a pattern with rotational symmetry.

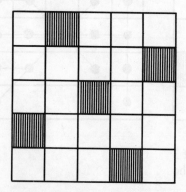

b

c   The remainder patterns after division by 3 or 6 are
    the same, making a magic square with three ones
    and two twos, in each row, column and diagonal,
    whose sum is 7. The pattern made after division by
    5 is also a magic square.

1	2	1	1	2
1	1	2	1	2
2	1	2	1	1
2	1	1	2	1
1	2	1	2	1

c(i)

2	4	1	2	2
1	2	2	2	4
2	2	4	1	2
4	1	2	2	2
2	2	2	4	1

c(ii)

10 *Geometrical puzzles*

Q1

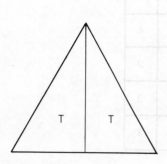 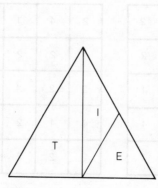

Q2 $R = \frac{1}{4}$

$T = \frac{1}{8}$

$E = \frac{1}{16}$

$I = \frac{1}{8}$

Q3

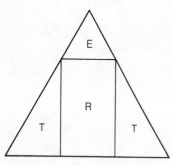

Q4

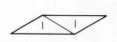

Q5

  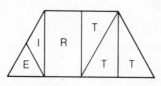 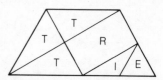

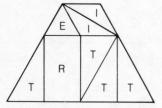 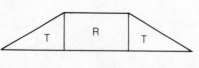 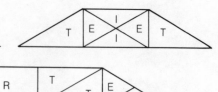

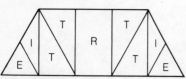 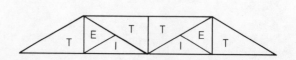

Q6

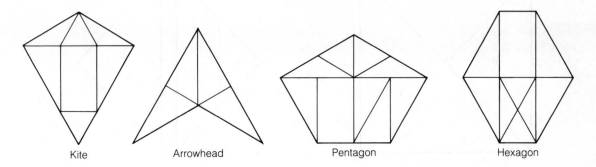

Kite   Arrowhead   Pentagon   Hexagon

Problems

1 *a* Q is a square; P is a parallelogram; the five triangular pieces are isosceles right-angled triangles of three different sizes.

b R and S are the same shape and size, and so are U and V.

c (i) An isosceles right-angled triangle; (ii) a square or a parallelogram.

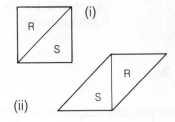

(i)

(ii)

d

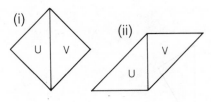

(i)   (ii)

e

f U, Q, V, P make an isosceles trapezium. P, V, Q, T make a cyclic quadrilateral, i.e. a circle can be drawn through its corners.

g All the pieces except Q have two angles equal to half a right-angle.

h The area of R and of S is $\frac{1}{4}$ of the area of the square T. P and Q are each ⅛, and U and V are each ¹⁄₁₆, of the area of the square.

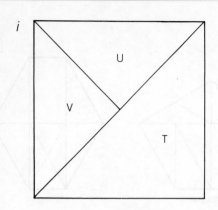

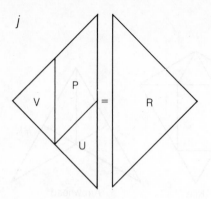

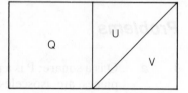

k   Each acute angle is half a right-angle, and each obtuse angle is $1\frac{1}{2}$ right-angles, a ratio of 1:3.

l   U, Q, V make an isosceles trapezium. The three pieces can be arranged to form a rectangle that is domino shaped.

2

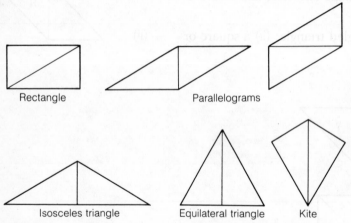

Rectangle   Parallelograms

Isosceles triangle   Equilateral triangle   Kite

b

c

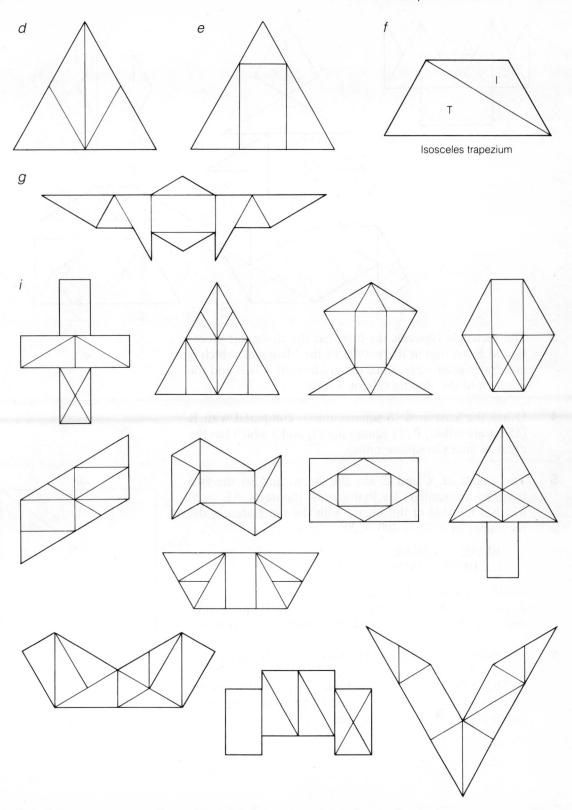

Isosceles trapezium

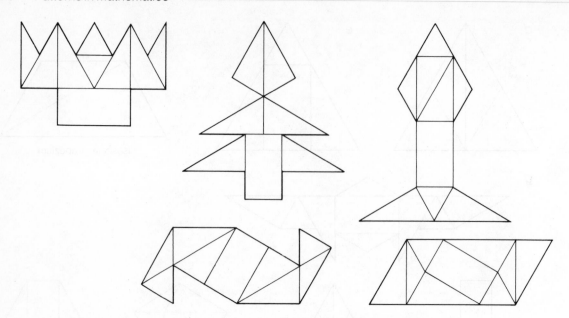

3   The rectangle conceals the fact that the triangular pieces Q and R overlap in the middle of the 'diagonal' which is not drawn accurately, since the gradient of R is ⅖ and the gradient of the sloping side of S is ⅓.

4   Q has the least area (8 square units), compared with R (15 square units), P (21 square units), and S which has the greatest area (26 square units).

5   The angles of X and Z are the same, and so the two triangles are similar. By Pythagoras' theorem, AE = 20 which is the side of the square with the same area as the rectangle, $16 \times 25 = 400 = 20^2$.

> BF/AB = AD/AE
> i.e. BF/25 = 16/20

So BF = 20, and AF = 15.
Area of X = 96 square units, area of Z = 150 square units and area of Y = 154 square units, which is the greatest.

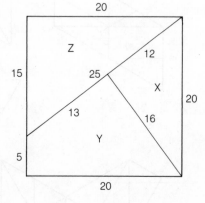

6   The ratio of white area to black area in each square is as follows: A, 50:50; B, 70:30; C, 50:50; D, 40:60; E, 70:30; F, 74:26. Thus D has the least white area, and F has the greatest white area, while A and C have the same area, and B and E have the same area.

7

Shape	Area in square units	Perimeter in units
P	44/100	4
Q	36/100	3
R	38/100	2.5
S	36/100	2.4
L	44/100	3.2
T	42/100	3.3

Note: the above answers are approximate only.

Hence P and L have the greatest area and P the greatest perimeter. Q and S have the least area, and S has the least perimeter.

8   The quadrilaterals have the following properties

Four equal sides	Four equal angles	Two pairs of equal sides	Two pairs of equal angles	One pair of equal sides	One pair of equal angles	No Parallel sides
S, D	S, R	P, K, A	P, D, K, I	I	K, A	K, A, Q, E, F

The semigrams and demi-semigrams are as follows:

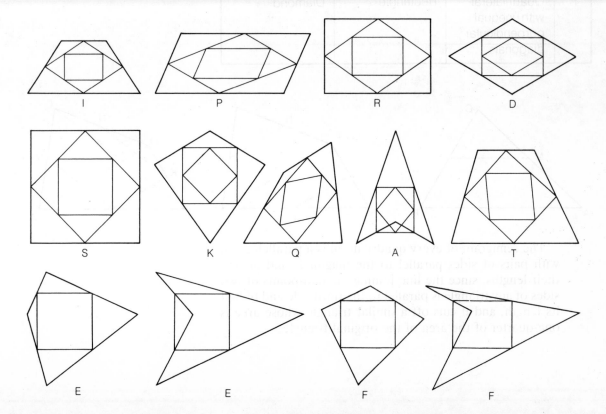

	Shape	Semigram	Demi-semigram
S	Square	Square	Square
R	Rectangle	Diamond	Rectangle
D	'Diamond' Rhombus	Rectangle	Diamond
P	Parallelogram	A different parallelogram	Parallelogram similar to the first parallelogram
T	Trapezium	Parallelogram	Parallelogram
I	Isosceles Trapezium	Diamond	Rectangle
K	'Kite'	Rectangle	Diamond
A	'Arrowhead'	Rectangle	Diamond
Q	Quadrilateral	Parallelogram	Parallelogram
E	Quadrilateral with equal perpendicular diagonals	Square	Square
F	Quadrilateral with unequal perpendicular diagonals	Rectangle	Diamond

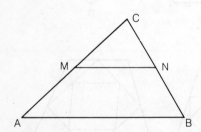 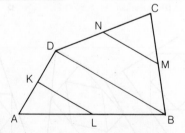 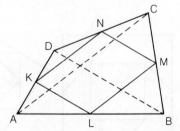

The semigram of every quadrilateral is a parallelogram with pairs of sides parallel to the diagonals and of half their lengths, since the line joining the mid-points of two sides of any triangle is parallel to the third side and of half its length, and it cuts off a similar triangle whose area is one-quarter of the area of the original triangle.

9

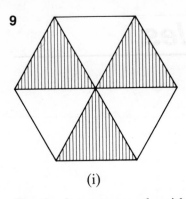

(i)

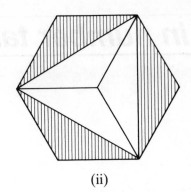

(ii)

Regular hexagons made with
(i) Six equilateral triangles
(ii) Six isosceles triangles

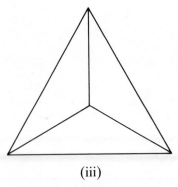

(iii)

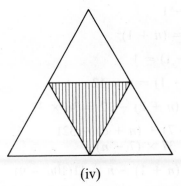

(iv)

Equilateral triangles made with
(iii) Three isosceles triangles
(iv) Four equilateral triangles

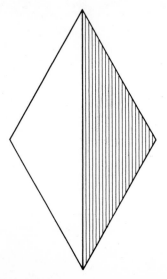

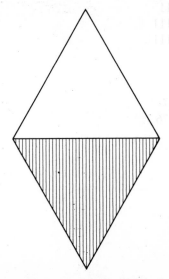

All the small diamonds in the pattern are the same in shape and size.

11 *Patterns in number tables*

Problems

1 *(1)* $n + (n + 1) - (n + 2) = n - 1$

  (2) $n + (n + 1) + (n + 2) - (n + 3) = 2n$

  (3) $n + (n \times n) = n(n + 1)$

  (4) $n^2 - (n - 1)^2 = 2n - 1$

  (5) $n(n + 1) + (n + 1) = (n + 1)^2$

  (6) $n \times n - (n + 1)(n - 1) = 1$

  (7) $(n - 1) + 10n + (n + 1) = n \times 12$

  (8) $100n + 10(n + 1) + (n + 2) - 12 = 3n \times 37$

  (9) $100(n + 8) + 10(n + 7) + (n + 6) - 321$
     $= 111n + 555 = 3 \times 37 \times (7 - n)$

  (10) $100(n - 1) + 10n + (n + 1) - n = 11(10n - 9)$

  (11) $(n - 1) + \ n + (n + 1) = 3n$

  (12) $1 + 3 + 5 + 7 + \ldots + (2n - 1) = n^2$

  (13)
$$\begin{aligned}
1 + 1 &= 2 \times 1 \\
12 + 21 &= 3 \times 11 \\
123 + 321 &= 4 \times 111 \\
1234 + 4321 &= 5 \times 1111
\end{aligned}$$

  (14)
$$\begin{aligned}
(8 \times 1) + 1 &= 9 \\
(8 \times 12) + 2 &= 98 \\
(8 \times 123) + 3 &= 987 \\
(8 \times 1234) + 4 &= 9876
\end{aligned}$$

  (15)
$$\begin{aligned}
1 - 1 &= 9 \times 0 \\
11 - 2 &= 9 \times 1 \\
111 - 3 &= 9 \times 12 \\
1111 - 4 &= 9 \times 123
\end{aligned}$$

(16)　　$(9 \times 9) + 7 = 88$
　　　　$(98 \times 9) + 6 = 888$
　　　$(987 \times 9) + 5 = 8888$
　$(9876 \times 9) + 4 = 88888$

(17)　　　$9 - \quad 1 = 8$
　　　　$98 - \quad 21 = 77$
　　　$987 - \quad 321 = 666$
　$9876 - 4321 = 5555$

(18)　　　　$9 - 1 \quad\quad = 8$
　　　　　$98 - 12 \quad\quad = 86$
　　　　$987 - 123 \quad\quad = 864$
　　$9876 - 1234 \quad\quad = 8642$
　$98765 - 12345 = 86420$

(19) $n - 2(n + 1) + (n + 2) = 0$

(20)　　$(7 \times 1) \quad\quad\quad + 1 = 8$
　　　　$(7 \times 12) \quad\quad\quad + 2 = 86$
　　　　$(7 \times 123) \quad\quad + 3 = 864$
　　　　$(7 \times 1234) \quad\quad + 4 = 8642$
　　　　$(7 \times 12345) + 5 = 86420$

(21)　　　$9 + 1 \quad\quad = 10 = \quad\quad 1$
　　　　$98 + 12 \quad\quad = 10 = \quad\quad 11$
　　　$987 + 123 \quad\quad = 10 = \quad 111$
　$9876 + 1234 = 10 = 1111$

(22) $(10 \times 0) \quad\quad + 1 = 1$
　　　$(10 \times 1) \quad\quad + 2 = 12$
　　　$(10 \times 12) \quad\quad + 3 = 123$
　　　$(10 \times 123) \quad + 4 = 1234$

(23) $(1 + 2 + 3 + \ldots + n)^2 = \frac{1}{4}n^2(n + 1)^2$
　　　　$= (1^3 + 2^3 + 3^3 + \ldots + n^3)$

(24) $(2n + 1) + (2n - 1) = 4n$

(25) $1 \times 7 \times 15873 = 111{,}111$
　　　$2 \times 7 \times 15873 = 222{,}222$
　　　$3 \times 7 \times 15873 = 333{,}333$

(26) $3 \times 7 \times 5291 = 111{,}111$
　　　$6 \times 7 \times 5291 = 222{,}222$
　　　$9 \times 7 \times 5291 = 333{,}333$

(27) $19 = 20 - 1$,　so　that　$n \times 19 = 10(2n - 1) + (10 - n)$, and $(2n - 1) + (10 - n) = n + 9$. In the multiplication table for 19, the tens digits form the sequence 1, 3, 5, 7, etc. and the units digits form the sequence 9, 8, 7, 6, etc.

a　$(2n)^2 - (2n - 2)^2 = 8n - 4 = 4(2n - 1)$, which produces the patterned sequence 4×1, 4×3, 4×5, 4×7 etc.

b　$(2n + 1)^2 - (2n - 1)^2 = 8n$, which is the sequence of multiples of 8.

c　$3367 \times 3 = 10101$. The sequence is 10101, 20202, 30303, . . ., 90909, 101010.

2　a　(i)　Chessboard pattern of alternating black and white cells;

(ii)　two diagonal lines — a bishop's move pattern;

(iii)　three parallel diagonal lines, moving downwards to the right;

(iv)　knight's move pattern moving downwards to the left;

(v)　a bishop's move pattern, except for the first number;

(vi)　a rook's move in a column;

(vii)　a short diagonal.

b　(i)　All arithmetic progressions with common difference of 6 lie on diagonals sloping down to the left.

(ii)　All arithmetic progressions with common difference 7 lie in vertical columns.

(iii)All arithmetic progressions with common difference 8 lie on diagonals sloping down to the right.

c　The totals in the three central columns are 75, 80, 85, which form an arithmetic progression with common difference 5. The totals in the three middle rows are 63, 112, 161, an arithmetic progression with common difference 49.

d　The numbers in the central column, middle row and both diagonals of any 3-by-3 square on a calendar are always arithmetic progressions whose sum is three times the number in the central cell. In the example, the sum is $3 \times 17 = 51$.